Triangle

by Arlene DeMarco

A SIGNET BOOK from
NEW AMERICAN LIBRARY
TIMES MIRROR

Library of Congress Catalog Card Number: 70-169064

This is a reprint of a hardcover edition published by The New American Library, Inc., and distributed by W. W. Norton & Company, Inc. The hardcover edition was published simultaneously in Canada by George J. McLeod, Ltd., Toronto.

SIGNET TRADEMARK REG. U.S. PAT. OFF. AND FOREIGN COUNTRIES
REGISTERED TRADEMARK—MARCA REGISTRADA
HECHO EN CHICAGO, U.S.A.

SIGNET, SIGNET CLASSICS, SIGNETTE, MENTOR AND PLUME BOOKS
are published by The New American Library, Inc.,
1301 Avenue of the Americas, New York, New York 10019

FIRST PRINTING, JUNE, 1972

PRINTED IN THE UNITED STATES OF AMERICA

The Beginning

"Nina, it's that Brace Fontaine. He's here!"

Would you believe it, he was! He flew in that morning from the coast and came straight from the airport, ready to move in and live with my family. Of course I had told Mom all about him when we got back from Vegas, because even though I really didn't expect him to follow through, I thought there was at least an outside chance he might and I didn't want her to be surprised.

"Honey," she said when I told her, "as long as he doesn't treat you like a good-time girl. You know, with these married men you have to be careful . . ."

ARLENE DEMARCO is the youngest of the five DeMarco sisters, whose singing team made show-business history. When she was five, she was doing five shows a day in vaudeville. When she was seven, she and her sisters were regulars on the Fred Allen Show. Arlene then had to stand on a box to reach the mike. Some years later Miss DeMarco left show business to devote her time to raising a family. She then went back into show business, singing in night-clubs and appearing as the featured guest on many major television shows.

Miss DeMarco was formerly married to a Hollywood actor from whom she is now separated, and she currently lives in the New York area with her two daughters, Rosana and Melisa. At the urging of many friends in show business, Miss DeMarco is again taking up her career in the entertainment world. This is her first novel.

Other SIGNET Titles
You Will Enjoy Reading

To Christopher

Chapter
ONE

I just figured out that the first six seconds of every tape are a gyp. You can't record on those first six seconds. Each tape costs three dollars and eighty-seven cents. And this is a one-hour tape we're talking about. So, I'm losing about six cents on each tape, right? Which is pretty good figuring for somebody who never finished junior high school.

Except I'm not losing the six cents. Herbie is, because Herbie buys me the tapes. Herbie bought me the recording outfit. A tape deck, he calls it. It's got everything. It's got a footage counter, which is a little dial where you can see the numbers that tell you how many feet of tape you've got left on the reel. It's got a little window where a red line bounces up and down and tells you when your voice is balanced. You can record from a radio or from a record player or even from the TV. You can record yourself or anybody you want on a mike. You can play the tapes through loudspeakers or your TV speaker or anything you hook it up to except maybe the shower. It's a very expensive thing, this tape deck. I saw it advertised in an RCA catalog that came in the mail around Christmas and it sold for four hundred and ninety-eight dollars —but why am I telling you all this? You already know all that because it's you, right? Anyhow, Herbie says that next Christmas, or maybe for my birthday, he's going to buy a couple of speakers for you. That is, if he's still hanging around by then—and if I don't hock you before then, so I'm not holding my breath and you shouldn't either.

Herbie's a jerkoff, but I like him. I don't like him as much as when I first met him because of that scene he pulled in the Poodle, but I still like him. All the same, he's still a jerkoff. He's like all the other jerkoffs who hang around me. There are always one or two. They're all alike. Mostly they're married, would you believe it? With kids and good-looking wives and homes in the suburbs. Herbie's a little different. He's not married and he lives in Manhattan and he doesn't have any kids that I know of. But he hangs around me for the same reason the other jerkoffs hang around. They all figure that sooner or later they're going to make it in bed with me. So does Herbie, but I think he'd like an exclusive arrangement. Not like married. I'm not that lucky, and anyhow I don't know if I want anything like that. I've been bitten already and, baby, have I got scars! No, Herbie doesn't want to marry me, but he would like something exclusive and regular. That's what he's holding out for. I mean, that's why he plays it cool with me. He's not like those other jokers who meet me, go out with me once, and right away their tongues are hanging out and they don't care if I know it.

They do anything for me, those guys, anything I want. Last week, this one jerkoff calls from his office to talk to me. At two o'clock in the afternoon he's just got to tell me how much he wants to see me again. He asks me what I'm doing because he wants to know if anybody else is maybe making time with me. I tell him I'm getting ready to take the kid to Bradley's for a pair of shoes. He wants to know how I'm getting there. I tell him I'm either calling a cab or maybe a girlfriend down the block will drive me.

"Stay there," he says. Like it's life or death. "I'm leaving right away."

He leaves his office, drives all the way from New York to Haverstraw where I live, drives us to Bradley's which is maybe all of two miles away, waits for me while I get Danny his shoes and do some shopping for cosmetics in Medi-Mart, drives us back home, finds out he can't hang around because my sister Dolores is in the house, and drives back to the city. Would you believe it? He left his business in the middle of the day, drove for almost an hour to my place, sat in his car in the parking lot for another hour, and then had to drive back to town in rush-hour traffic. For what! So he could say maybe three words to me, because, after all, how much can you say in front of a bright five-year-old like Danny? That's why he's a jerkoff. He thinks he's running up a score with me like on a pinball machine. If he hits enough bumpers the numbers will add up and the lights will go on and the bells will ring and there I'll be waiting for him in bed with my legs spread. He's crazy!

8

That's why Herbie bought me you. He's crazy, too. I met Herbie on Madison Avenue. I was looking in a dress shop window and I turned to cross the street when the light changed and there was this tall, good-looking young guy staring at me. I knew he was in show business. I just knew it. I could tell by the way he was dressed, sort of careless but like he thought about it first, and with the long sideburns, and the long hair coming over the tops of his ears and poking out over his coat collar. Uncombed, but combed. The Richard Burton look, know what I mean? I also knew that look on his face. Herbie was saying to himself, What a doll! Would I love to lay that!

I had a reaction to him, too, I must admit. I always react to that type of man. You know, they're young and tall and good-looking. Just like me, real beautiful people; like the young girls and boys you see on airline commercials about Bermuda. Whenever I meet a guy like that I always think what a great bed team we'd make, two good-looking young healthy bodies together on one mattress. Because they don't know how old I really am. I still look like twenty, don't I? Well, I do. Take my word for it. That's what you'd say if you could see me.

Cool it, I said to myself. You're acting like you're seventeen.

But it was too late. Herbie saw how I looked at him, and he started talking to me. So, I talked back while we walked along, and sure enough, he turned out to be a TV actor. He was doing pretty good in a daytime soap, knocking down a grand a week, which, while it doesn't compare to the seventy grand Brace used to make in a week, is not to be sneezed at. These days I don't sneeze at a weekly C-note, let alone a grand. I mean, to me at the moment, that's money, baby.

Anyway, I was on my way to the Port Authority terminal to get the bus home, but Herbie had his Austin-Healy in the RCA building garage, so he drove me. We started going out and for a while it was great between us. No pressure, no pushing, no pulling, no trying to get me into a motel or anything like that. It was just fun. I dug Herbie and he dug me. I really thought that maybe this was going to turn out to be something. Usually when I go out with a man, I don't expect anything but the usual fooling around which is supposed to put me in the mood for a night of fucking. With Herbie, I began hoping that, maybe, this time, things would be different. I thought that maybe this one was interested in me as a person and not

9

as something beautiful with a convenient hole that he could show off to his friends and say, "Get a load of this beautiful doll I'm making it with."

Herbie was great with Danny. The kid really liked him and still does. A couple of times he took him out to the park and to museums, and he played ball with him once or twice. Which is great because I know that Danny needs a father. Believe me, if anybody knows how much a kid needs a father, it's me. And I had one, but I didn't, if you know what I mean! I try to be everything to Danny, but it's good for him to have a man around once in a while, right?

Then one Saturday night, Herbie took me to the Show Stoppers. I didn't want to go. I hadn't been there since the night Chuck went after me. I tried to get Herbie to change his mind, but he insisted because his agent had told him it was time he was seen in places where the important people hang out. He told Herbie to get himself a swell-looking date and he'd have a photographer on hand to catch the act. The photographer never showed up, which is just as well, otherwise he would have caught Herbie in an act his agent didn't bargain for.

Against my better judgment we went. I looked gorgeous. When I split with Brace, I managed to get out of the apartment with enough clothes to fill three valises, and I made sure my evening gowns were included. This one fitted me like a Jell-O mold. I've got a great figure to begin with, with long svelte curves around the hips and down the outside of the thighs. In a mini my legs are so good, especially around the thighs, men can't keep their eyes on my face. I will admit that I am a little light on top. I'm not flat, don't get me wrong. I'm a good thirty-six, sort of low slung and full. I've never had any complaints, but a Sophia Loren or a Raquel Welch I'm not. Anyhow, with the way this dress is divided down the front, I could have had zero and it wouldn't have mattered, because there was no brassiere visible, only lots of visible me right down to the Chinese salt cellar. I thought Herbie would flip his zipper when he picked me up that night. All the way driving in, I had to remind him to keep his eyes on the road. Once or twice I thought he forgot why we were going out. I kept expecting him to pull into a motel instead. He had *that* look on his face.

Clyde, the maitre d', recognized me right away.

"Good to see you again, Miss Brandi," he said and took us to a very good table, better than Herbie deserved.

10

Herbie never noticed. He was making an entrance, playing it cool like he came to the Show Stoppers every other night, at least. I almost died laughing inside.

We weren't there two minutes before people started whispering. Herbie didn't notice that either. He was too busy looking for celebrities and wondering when the photographer would show up. I saw familiar faces at nearby tables and I could pick up some of the talk buzzing around us. Most of it was coming from people who were too embarrassed to come over to say hello. Everybody knows what happened there. In fact a lot of people who were there right that minute had been on the scene when the well-known Chuckee-boy blew his cork.

The first one to break the ice was Mickey Faye. Mickey doesn't give a shit for anyone or anything. Mickey always goes his own way. That's one of the reasons why he's such a headliner. When I saw him coming I turned my head away, but he stopped as Clyde led him to his table.

"Hey, look who came in," whispered Herbie, happy that the celebrities were arriving at last. "I think it's—" and then his voice cut off and he had a funny look on his face. Here comes Mickey straight for us, gangling, six-foot Mickey with his long, thin face all lit up like the Rockefeller Center Christmas tree and his hands stretched out.

"Nina, baby! Where you been! Good to see you again!"

And then came a big smack on the cheek and the peck on the lips like he always does to me with his lips all pushed up together so I know it's not for real.

All the time I was married, I heard that he was always asking for me, and how sorry he was when things went sour between me and Brace. Believe me, there was many a day and lots of nights when I missed that sad, funny man.

"Back in circulation again?" and he gave me that sad little smile that always grabs his audience when he's reaching for tears.

"Just a little, Mickey."

I gave him my big-brave-girl smile.

"Good. I'm glad. Come see me later. I'll be sitting right over there."

And off he went, waving his hands at someone else and leaving Herbie ready to fall out of his chair.

"That was Mickey Faye," he said, like he was waking up.

I played it cool. I didn't want to go in for any long

11

explanations. Not just then. "Sorry, I didn't have a chance to introduce you, Herbie."

"That's all right. You know him?"

What a stupid question!

I should have told him, No, Mickey always plays big scenes with total strangers!

Instead I said, "We were good friends once."

Herbie's eyes narrowed. "Good friends."

"That's all. Just good friends."

Which was the absolute truth. I could see that Herbie didn't believe me. Personally, I couldn't have cared less. It just showed how ignorant and out of the know he was; otherwise he would have known what everybody knows, that Mickey doesn't have girlfriends. He has quickies in his dressing room before the show. For that you don't need girlfriends, just girls.

"I know you used to be in show business," Herbie said, "but I didn't know you knew any of the big ones. Not like Mickey Faye."

"You'd be surprised who I used to know," I told him with a straight face, which is also the truth. He would have been surprised if he'd ever given me a chance to tell him about that part of my life, but he was always too busy talking about himself. And he would have been surprised to know that in my life I've gone from chauffeured limousines and expensive co-op apartments to relief, which is where I'm at now.

Sam and Joye Garrick were the next to come over, which was no surprise. I expected them. After all, we're old friends. They used to be at the apartment regularly, and Brace and I went out with them a lot. Even today, Joye calls me up once in a while to see how I am. The Garricks are a great team, a husband-and-wife movie producing and writing team. She writes them and co-produces with Sam, who's very big on promotion and working out distribution deals. The one big box office smash they had was from a book that Joye wrote. It made the best-seller list, then they parlayed it into a film and made millions on the whole deal. I was in it, and so were Brace and Chuck, because she got a lot of the story from me, but I never held it against her. Why should I? Hell, there's nothing exclusive about me, only to myself. There's nothing exclusive about any of us, right?

"Darling," Joye said as she pressed her cheek to mine. "You've finally made the effort. Hello." That was to Herbie. "I'm Joye Garrick. My husband, Sam. Darling, I told you ages ago you should get out. Anyhow you did, that's what's important. I always knew you would. Didn't I, Sam? Didn't I say she has guts?"

"We both said it," Sam said, leaning over Herbie's shoulder to shake my hand. "Good to see you again, kiddo. Let's hear from you once in a while. Maybe I can do something."

Sam's eyes stayed too long on my Great Divide, so Joye took his arm and pulled him back a little.

"We're all going on to Yellowfingers for laughs. Why don't you come too?"

I really wanted to, but I said no. It was a big temptation. I don't get to go out on the town that often, not for a real evening's worth. Married men being what they are don't like to be seen in popular places. This time I was out with a single guy, but I knew that Joye and Sam and their crowd could drop hundreds of dollars in one night and never miss it, and I wasn't sure if Herbie was well-heeled, so I begged off.

You think he appreciated it? He missed the point completely. And then he started getting up-tight. All evening people kept coming over to say hello, and Herbie got quieter and quieter until I could see he was really stewing inside. I knew what was bothering him. Herbie was jealous. And mad. Here he had brought this swell-looking dish to the grooviest place in town, expecting everybody to look at him and take notice, and instead the dish was getting all the action. He could have stayed home for all the mileage he was getting out of the scene.

I think the straw that broke Herbie's back was when George Cobb came over for an item for "Cobb's Corner." I thought this was maybe a good chance to save the evening for Herb, so I gave it the old college try.

"George," I said, "Herbie's got a regular lead on 'Always Tomorrow' on NBC. You should talk to him about it. Some of the stories he tells me—honest, even for television it's too much!"

"Maybe I will sometime," George said and turned back to me. "But what about you, Nina? Where've you been hiding for the last two years? Any plans you can tell me about? I heard Bobby asked you back on 'Manhattan Midnight.'"

"If he did, then vaudeville's back at the Palace," I said. The one and only time Bobby Casey had me on the show he was beaten up because of it. If vaudeville's had its day, so has Nina Brandi as far as Bobby Casey is concerned.

Just about then, Herbie got up and left without saying anything. I found him a half hour later at the bar drinking double scotches. I don't have much patience anymore with men when they start acting like spoiled brats. I said to myself, Screw you, you bastard, and asked him to take me home. He didn't say two words all the way up the West Side and across the bridge, but by the time we were up the parkway near our exit, he brightened up enough to suggest going to a bar for a nightcap. He doesn't know the local spots, so I suggested the Pink Poodle, which is a fun place. The crowd is young, and though I'm over thirty, and out of their scene, I like to sit there and watch and wish I'd had time in my life for the kinds of things kids were doing when I was that age.

It wasn't a good idea. Jack Crown, the bartender, is an old fan of mine. Usually when I'm there alone I sit at the bar and talk to him. That night Herbie and I sat at a table and we were all dressed up like we'd just come from the Persian Room. It really got to Jack, because for the first time since I've been dropping in at the place, he told some of the kids who I was. I guess he thought I'd get a kick out of it, which I must admit I did, but for Herbie it was the Show Stoppers all over again. Some of the kids came to the table and asked me to sing, but I don't really know any of their songs and they'd only think my old numbers were corny, so I said my throat was sore. Then one kid ran home and came back with—would you believe it?—one of the albums I cut with my sisters years ago. He said he took it out of his father's collection and he thought his dad would get a big kick out of it if I autographed it, which was a sweet thought. At least to me it was, but not to Herbie. By that time he had had another two or three double scotches and he was really feeling his load.

"Hey, look who's here!" he started saying in a loud voice. "It's Nina Brandi. Anybody remember Nina Brandi? Hey, will you look who I'm out with? A real celebrity! Nina Brandi! How about that? She was in the Top Ten in nineteen forty-two and a half all the way back there. How about that?"

"It was nineteen forty-five and it was the Camel Hit Parade," I told him. "And you can go straight to hell, you shitty bastard." And I got up and left him sitting there and walked all the way home.

I didn't see Herbie for two weeks after that. It could have been two years for all I cared. Or two hundred. Then one day he showed up with the tape deck—that's

14

you—and a guy to install you and show me how you work. It was his way of trying to make it up to me.

I wasn't as mad at him anymore, but the bloom was off the roses, as they used to say. With Herbie it's as plain as day that he won't be able to do me any good until he stops thinking so much about himself. Maybe that's my hang-up, too. Everybody in show business, or who was ever in show business, has a big ego, know what I mean? It's vanity. That's what keeps you going a lot of the time, no matter how much talent you have or haven't got, because look at all the people around with talent who never get anywhere. No ego.

Anyhow, these days I give everything I've got in me to Danny. I really live for him. He's everything to me, even if once in a while I do let my big fat ego carry me away. Not that I'd ever leave Danny, don't get me wrong. Don't think that. I never would. Never! He means too much to me. If I'm nothing else, I think I'm a damn good mother. I'm always here for him when he needs me. I go to the PTA teas and I'm class mother and that kid gets my love like no one ever did before. And he loves me right back like no one ever did, too, with no favors asked. It's strange and wonderful, I guess, that Danny and this love we have for each other could come out of all that shit I had to go through with Brace, but there it is, and here we are.

And here we are, you and me, constant companions in the cold, lonely nights. You're really a good thing for me, you know that? Any night I can't sleep, I can just talk to you and you talk back and that's the reason for our great and lasting friendship. I don't know how I would ever be able to make any sense out of everything that's happened if I couldn't talk like this to you and you didn't talk back and say the things I want to hear. Of course, sometimes the way they come out, I really don't want to hear them. I really want to switch you off, but I can't. I can't shut my ears and not listen, because I know I have to listen.

God! I say to myself. Was that me? Did it really happen like that? God, how could you let it?

But He did, and it happened, and maybe, someday, I'll get it all straight in my mind so I can stop bugging myself with when and how and why did it ever start.

Chapter
TWO

I don't know the why or the how but I remember the when. It started on a rainy day in Manhattan on the Upper West Side. There are a million stories in the Naked City! Remember that one? Anyhow ...

My roommate Billie Adelle and I both had the day off. I was sitting around looking through the *Daily News* when I got to the entertainment section and saw that Val Winters was headlining at the Roxy. Val is an old friend of mine from way back. I've known him since I was about six years old and he was thirteen or fourteen and we were sharing the same bill at some vaudeville mill in Chicago. He used to take me out between shows and buy me ice cream cones and candy. Val was a long way up the ladder since then. He was very popular with that velvety soft voice of his that made all the middle-aged women fall all over themselves and cream in their pants, and now there he was headlining at the Roxy with his own show.

Fifteen minutes later, Billie and I were on the Broadway bus headed downtown and about an hour after that I was watching a stand-up comic by the name of Jerry Miller doing his stuff. He was kind of short, a not-too-good-looking guy, not my type at all, and he kept looking at me all through his act. We were sitting in about the fifth row dead center and he was downstage at the foots, so we could see each other at close range. All the time he was on, he kept looking at me, and for some reason I couldn't take my eyes off him. Sounds corny, doesn't it? Well truth is stranger than fiction, isn't that what they say, and there he was and there was I, hooked!

Then Val came on and all through his songs, instead of listening to him like a good friend, I kept thinking of Jerry Miller. You know what I was thinking? I was thinking, Why am I thinking about him? His personality onstage was not the greatest and his material wasn't much better. He hadn't made me laugh even once. And it wasn't his face either, because he didn't look like anything special. In fact, looking at him you'd never think he was a comic or in show business. He looked more like he held down some

16

ordinary kind of job like a salesman or maybe a teacher. So what was there about him that got to me? I finally decided that it was something about his eyes. I once read in a magazine that all comedians are sad, frustrated people—you know, the laugh clown laugh routine—and maybe that's what there was about Jerry that hit me right where it counted.

After the stage show we went backstage to see Val, and on the way I told Billie how I felt. She looked at me like I was loose between the ears.

"Nina, that's crazy!" she said. "What's with you? You've never even been to bed with a man. You've had no experience at all."

Which was a pretty hard argument for me to answer because Billie at the time had all of two affairs behind her, and that was two up on me, right?

The first thing I said to Val after we said hello and kissed each other was, "Is that comic here? You know, the one who was on with you?"

"Forget it, Nina," he said. "He's married."

My heart dropped faster than the elevators in the RCA building.

"OK. He's married," I said. "Well, you were very good anyhow."

Val and Billie laughed.

"You don't mean to say you really go for him?" Val said.

"Suppose I do. So what?"

"Well, for one thing, he's much older than you."

"So what else is new?" I said, looking sidewise at Billie, who couldn't stop laughing.

My sisters and I were singing at the Tropicana at night and rehearsing a television show during the afternoon, so I really didn't have much time to concentrate on Jerry Miller, but he was always there hiding in the back of my mind, sneaking around behind my thoughts.

Every once in a while I would stop whatever I was doing and think to myself, I wonder what he's doing right now, right this minute.

It got to be a kind of game with me during coffee breaks and waiting for camera cues, and once I said it out loud without knowing it, because my sister Angie, who was standing next to me, turned around and said, "What did you say?"

So I told her about Jerry. Angie is the oldest of the four of us and the one I always confide in right to this day. She

17

just laughed about it and told me I'd get over it, but the guy kept bugging me.

About two weeks later, we were rehearsing at this old movie theater on Fifty-first Street which had just been made into a television studio. They were just starting to do that with a lot of movie houses that weren't paying off anymore and even some legit houses. At lunchtime my sisters wanted to eat at Mama Leone's but I said, "No, I want to eat at Clark's. Please, let's go there. It's just down the block on Eighth. We can grab a sandwich and Coke. Mama Leone's will take too long. Clark's please!"

Clark's was a drugstore that also had a lunch counter with booths, and it was very popular with show business people at that time. That's why I wanted to go. I knew what I was doing, but I was afraid to do it alone. I wanted my sisters along for moral support, except that what happened later on, because we went to Clark's that day, didn't turn out to be so moral.

I had a hunch that Jerry would be having lunch there. All that morning during rehearsal I kept saying to myself, I'll bet he eats at Clark's. I had to see him again. I knew I was probably nuts for thinking so much about him, but I just had to see him. Would you believe it, that a girl could carry on like that over some guy she'd never met, a guy she'd seen only once before after being on her own in New York for only six weeks?

When we got to Clark's, I walked in ahead of the others, spotted an empty booth, and went right for it. While I was taking off my coat and hanging it up, I had a good chance to look around without being too obvious. I saw the usual familiar faces and then up the aisle, at the back near the door to the kitchen, I saw these three guys. Two of them were pretty well-known comics who were on the way up then. The third member of the party was Jerry Miller, and he was looking right at me.

"There's that comic I told you about," I said to Angie in a low voice as I sat down. "Back in the corner booth."

Angie gave a good look and sat down opposite me.

"What's happened to your taste?"

"I don't know. He just does something to me. And now he's looking at me again."

"I think you'd better stick to a sandwich and Coke today because you're a little mixed up."

"That's what Billie told me two weeks ago, but it didn't help."

We had a good laugh and then we all gave our orders

18

to the waitress. Five minutes later, I saw Angie look up and stop chewing. I turned to see what she was looking at, and there was Jerry Miller standing over us.

"You must be the Brandi Sisters," he said.

"Yes, we are," I said with my mouth full of bacon and tomato and my stomach full of butterflies.

"I'd like to introduce myself . . ." he started to say, when I cut in with, "I know who you are."

"And I know who you are. You're Nina."

"That's right."

"Well, I'm—"

"You're Jerry Miller—I saw you a couple of weeks ago at the Roxy and I really thought you were sensational."

He stood there looking down at me, not knowing what to say after that. My sisters went on eating and looking at the both of us and at each other.

"Excuse me," he said to Angie. "May I borrow your kid sister for a while? Will you sit down and have a cup of coffee with me, or a Coke or something?"

"Why not?" I said, and forgetting all about my sandwich, I got up and walked back to his table, which was now deserted. As I went, I took a fast peek back at my sisters. They were staring after me with their mouths open like they thought I was nuts or something. Then we were sitting down looking at each other across a lot of dirty plates and cups half-filled with cold coffee and ashtrays full of butts. Very romantic, right? The waitress took our order for two coffees and went away.

"Before we go any further," Jerry said, "let me lay my cards on the table for you."

"Go ahead." I tried to sound like I was talking business with a theater manager but I felt a little out of breath. I think I was expecting him to say, Will you marry me right away, or something like that.

"I'm married," he said, "but my wife is living in Florida."

I was stunned for a minute because what he said was so close to what I was thinking. Then I started to laugh and he looked at me like I was crazy.

"What are you laughing at?"

"I can't help it. It's just like that joke. You know, the one about the guy in Florida who tries to pick up this girl on the beach. It's OK, he tells her, I can take you out because I'm separated. My wife's up in the room."

Jerry leaned back and laughed.

19

"That's pretty good," he said. "And it fits. I'm separated, too. Legally separated."

"Yes, well you're still married as far as I'm concerned. Is that what you wanted to tell me?"

"No, not quite. I wanted to tell you that a year ago I saw you at the Fox in St. Louis."

"You mean the time we were there with Al Martino and Shecky Greene?"

"Right. I was in the audience and I fell in love with you while I was watching you on the stage."

Now it was my time to sit back and look amazed. The only thing I could think of was to stall.

My father always used to say, When you meet men, as you will in life sooner or later, you must play hard to get because a man doesn't like a girl who is easy or falls all over him. Corny, but believe me it has its points, and I guess I really had taken it to heart because right at that moment what I really wanted to say was—what a coincidence! I fell in love with you when I saw you onstage at the Roxy. Only I was too arrogant and proud to let him know how I felt that early in the game, so I pushed the thought away. Instead I said, "Oh, really?" as though I was used to hearing this from men every other day.

"You said you caught me at the Roxy. How did you like my act?"

"Well, I really went there to see Val Winters. He's an old friend and you just happened to be on the same bill."

He looked so disappointed I felt like telling him the truth right then and there.

"You were very good, too," I said. "Didn't you hear what I said before? I thought you were sensational."

His face brightened up and he smiled.

"I'd like to take you out tonight."

"That's out of the question." I had answered without thinking. He was going a little too fast for me.

"You have a date already?"

"No."

"A rehearsal?"

"Not exactly."

"You'll be in town, won't you?"

"I live in town."

"Oh?"

"I moved into town about six weeks ago. I share an apartment with a girlfriend."

"Really."

Inexperienced as I was, I thought I heard something in

his voice that made me look at him closely, but he looked back without blinking an eye and we sat there looking at each other without speaking for a minute. I drank some coffee and put the cup down. My mind was made up.

"We're doing a television show tonight at the old Playhouse right up the block."

"I know where it is."

"I'll go out with you after the show."

"What time will that be?"

"Air time is eight. We'll be off by nine. Give me twenty minutes to get out of costume and makeup."

"See you at the stage door."

He picked up the check and walked down the aisle. I waited until he was at the cashier's before I went back to my sisters' table.

"What's the matter with you?" Dolores wanted to know as I sat down. "You're as white as a ghost."

I didn't answer.

Angie said, "Well something happened, because you certainly look different since you went over there with what's-his-name."

"I'm all right."

"I hope so, because we were talking to some people while you two were having your little tête-à-tête and found out that the guy is married."

"I know that."

"We also found out that he's older than you," Marcie said. "By about twelve years."

I hadn't realized he was that much older but I didn't want them to know that, so I said, "I know what's going on. He just wants to go out and have coffee or something after the show. Maybe a drink."

"Oh, really!" Marcie said.

"We might even go to a club or something," I told them, putting my chin up and trying to look very nonchalant about the whole thing.

"You better watch where you go and what you do with that one, honey," Dolores chimed in, in her usual bitchy way.

"Look," I said, losing my temper a little. "I've had to listen to this kind of crap long enough. Thanks for your opinion but I'm going out with him anyhow. I'm eighteen now and I'm on my own, so lay off. I'm very attracted to this guy and I want to see what he's like."

We left it at that. We finished our lunch, went back to the studio, and went on with the rehearsal. I spent the rest of the afternoon with my mind in a turmoil, goofing up the lyrics and making the director tear out his hair while we went over the same song fifty times. Finally I got it right. The song, I mean.

Chapter
THREE

When the show was over and the floor manager yelled, "It's a wrap!" I headed right for the dressing room. Usually I would stand around with my sisters and have a few words with the orchestra leader and maybe the other talent about how well the show went and how our numbers went over, but this time I got out of my gown and makeup and into a pair of slacks in nothing flat. Jerry was there, just like he said he would be, waiting at the stage door.

He didn't say a word. No "you look great," not even "hello." He just held out his arm like he wanted me to take it and I put my hand on it, and we started down the street. I felt so—it's hard to describe. Being a machine, you wouldn't understand because you don't have feelings, but any woman would. I was thrilled to be with him. All the guys I had been out with before were all young and good-looking and debonair, which was the style then. Yet there I was stepping out with this innocuous type of guy who was not really good-looking at all, who was so much older than me, and loving it.

We went to a restaurant; I don't remember the name. I don't think I even noticed at the time, I was that mesmerized. He said, "In here," and we went in and sat down at a table and looked at each other. Somewhere on the edge of the scene there was a waiter, until Jerry ordered something and we were alone and we started to say things to each other.

He said something like "It's going to be very hard for you to believe this, but I really did fall in love with you last year."

And I said something like "I know you're much older than I am and you've probably had all the experience in the world, so I want to tell you right off the bat that I am not experienced. I'm still a virgin."

22

When I told him that, he looked like I was trying to put him on.

"Come on!" he said.

"Oh, I know what you think. I've been in the business since I was five and the Brandi Sisters have traveled all over and I've really been around a lot and all that. Well, believe it or not, I'm untouched. And what's more, two of my sisters are married and the other two of us are virtuous girls."

"You must have led a pretty protected kind of life. Somebody really must have been watching over you."

"Somebody always was."

"Is that why you moved to the city and out on your own?"

If I get to sound like a bitter bitch right about here, it's because so many years later I can read between the lines of the script. I know how it went and how it ended. The Roxy and Clark's were just curtain-raisers. This little scene is when the action really started. This is where they said "lights, camera, action," because this was when I opened up to Jerry, when my emotions really got all tangled up around him. Before it was just some kind of unexplainable physical or personality attraction, but now here he was wanting to know all about me and being so interested.

I told Jerry all about my life, about how poor my family always was and how we struggled to make the big time in show business, how my father got us started as a singing sister act, the Brandi Sisters, and how we used to sing at neighborhood block parties in Brooklyn where we lived and church suppers and things like that. I told him about traveling around with Dad playing cheap vaudeville dates, then cutting a couple of records, and then singing on the Frank Ellis show on network radio, which was our first big break. I went through the whole bit, including how Dad died soon after we became successful and how our agent put us on the vaudeville circuit and when I got to be eighteen how we started playing club dates. I also told him that I got so tired of being the youngest and being watched over by everybody that I finally had to get out on my own and see the world.

When I finished, he sat there and looked at me without saying anything. Then he reached across the table and took my hand and squeezed it.

"Maybe I'll see the world with you," he said in a quiet, gentle voice.

23

That's just the way it happened, so help me. Can you believe it!

That was the beginning of our relationship. We started going out together about as much as two people in show business can, which is always a problem. Either I was in Chicago while he was in Pittsburgh or I was getting ready to leave for St. Louis when he was coming in from the coast. But we managed. Whenever we were both in New York, we got together in our free time and it got to be a very steady thing between us.

He even drove out to Brooklyn with me to meet my mother. She was living in the house we bought for her after Dad died. Mom was crazy about him. Of all my men, he was the one she really dug. He wasn't the usual kind of wise-guy jerkoff you meet in the business, the loudmouth comic who's always doing his thing and never comes offstage. He was a real person, like the Jewish people say, a *mensch*, which somebody told me means a real man, someone you could touch and feel and talk to and believe in. I guess that's what got to her. And when I saw how much she liked him, that only made me fall for him the harder, because of all the people in my life, I loved my mother the most.

This went on between us for about four or five months. I don't think I ever touched the ground that whole time. I was floating. Everything was like a dream. Even when I wasn't with him and I was just marking time waiting until I saw him again, the thought that I would see him again and how it was between us was enough to keep me off the ground.

During all that time, I never went to bed with him, not once. It wasn't because he didn't want me to, but at first I was too afraid. We kissed and necked in his car and things like that, but that was as far as it went. I always found some kind of excuse to wriggle away and run home before he could pin me down. When he brought me home after a date, I would say that Billie was coming back soon. If he came up with me to the apartment door, I would say she wasn't feeling well and I had to get inside in a hurry to see how she was. Oh, I was very subtle. I had a thousand excuses and he saw through every one, but I was so inexperienced I was sure we would go on like that as long as I wanted.

If I'm being honest with you all the way, I have to admit that after we'd been going together for a couple of months, I wanted to go to bed with him. You see, in spite

24

of my fears I was curious. I wanted to know what all the fuss was about. Billie gave me a blow-by-blow description of what it's like, and that's not a joke because Billie doesn't go down on anyone, but I was all hot about experiencing life on my own and I knew that I wouldn't be satisfied until I'd been to bed with a man myself. Once in a while I wanted to give in. I really did, only I didn't seem to be able to get myself to say yes. Sometimes when he gave me very long, passionate kisses and his tongue rubbed tips with mine, I would get so weak in the knees and wet between the legs, it was all I could do to stay up on my feet. But I held out. Partly it was because I had this feeling about myself, my vanity I guess it was, that I did not want to be "devirginized," I guess you could call it. And partly it was because he was still married. Even though he kept telling me that he was going to get a divorce and hinted a couple of times about us getting married, a bell would go *ting!* in the back of my head and I would get the feeling that the whole thing between us was unstable. It just didn't seem like something I could count on. See, I was still very romantic, the way girls are at that age, and even though I was curious, it wasn't so much sex with me as the courtship that counted. Besides, as I know now, what I felt for Jerry was more than just sex. I could sit with him in a restaurant or just be in the same room with him and that was enough for me. He was there where I could look at him and hear his voice and see his eyes whenever he looked at me, and I was satisfied with just that.

Early in November he went to Las Vegas to play a date at the Last Frontier, and while he was there he was also signed for the Sands and then for the Castaways, two weeks at each, so he was gone for six weeks. In the meantime we went into the Tropicana with Tony Martin heading the bill. The Four Brandi Sisters were the extra added attraction, and when Jerry came back from Vegas, he joined the bill as the featured comic. I remember it was just before Christmas but I didn't know he was back in New York until I saw him at the first runthrough. I was surprised and shocked because usually the first thing he did when he got back into town was to call me up.

"Guess who, baby," he would whisper into the phone, and my heart would go up into my throat and beat triple time and I'd start running around pulling dresses out of the closet and yelling at Billie to give me the hair curlers. This time there was no phone call and no Jerry in New

York as far as I was concerned, until there he was, talking to the director and looking over at me where I was sitting with my sisters waiting for things to get started.

"Why doesn't he come over and say hello?"

"Honey, he's talking to Tony. Nobody turns his back on the star of the show, you know that. Now will you forget him and get with it!"

Angie was trying to calm me down and get me ready for our first number.

"What's the matter with you? Don't you have any pride?" Dolores hissed in my ear. "Stop throwing yourself at the guy, will you? Everybody in town's talking about the way you're carrying on with him."

I held out until the crew broke for lunch. Then I swallowed my pride and went over to him. He was talking with his manager who had dropped in to watch the run-through, but when he saw me coming he said something and his manager left.

He turned his head so I had to kiss him on the cheek.

"When did you get back?"

"Day before yesterday."

"How come you didn't call?"

"Didn't have time. I've been busy."

By this time even I could see that something was wrong. It was taking a little time for me to appreciate the fact that he could be so cool to me when just two short months ago he couldn't get enough of me, but I was learning to appreciate it very fast, believe me.

"Is everything all right?"

"Everything's fine. I have a girlfriend that I'm seeing a lot and I'm very serious about her."

It hit me like a punch in the stomach. I felt my face go white and for a minute I couldn't catch my breath. When I tried to talk I had to make such an effort my throat hurt.

"You've got to be kidding!"

"No, I'm not. In fact, I'm meeting her folks after the show tonight."

He said it as though he was telling me that he was going out to buy a new hat. Then the makeup man came over, so he had to sit down and be fussed over and we couldn't talk anymore.

I couldn't believe it. I just couldn't believe that he was serious. I was sure he was playing some kind of practical joke on me, that's how big my ego was in those days. Well, it got taken down a little that night. I was sitting in the lounge with my sisters after the show when this cute-looking chick showed up. I knew it was her as soon as she walked in. For one thing she had an older man and woman with her, the visiting fireman and his wife types, looking like they had just got off the bus from Hayseed Corners. For another thing, she reminded me of myself. There was something about her, maybe her age, because she looked as young as me and had my coloring and hair. The more I looked at her and studied her, the more I could see that she was practically my double, which made me feel even worse. It was a real blow to my ego because I couldn't see what was so different about this girl that made Jerry throw me over for her.

Then Jerry came in and went over to her and I saw the difference. It was in the way they looked at each other, how their hands touched and held on, how she leaned against him. It was the way my sister Angie had acted with her husband after they came back from their honeymoon. Jerry and this girl had been to bed together, that was the difference.

After a number of crying fits, with Billie trying to comfort me and my sisters walking around muttering about how he wouldn't get away with this if Pop was still alive, I tried to make some sense out of it in my own mind. But no matter how many different answers I tried on, I kept winding up with the same one.

I had to know. I couldn't just walk away and let the thing die, so I waited until I could get him alone backstage when no one else was around and then I confronted him.

"Tell me something, Jerry," I said. "This new love that you've found and this new relationship and the ending of our romance and everything. Could sex have anything to do with it?"

"Sex has everything to do with it."

I had just been handed free, for nothing, Lesson Number One About Men. It's too bad I didn't pay attention.

"You know how I care for you, Jerry. I think I really love you."

"That has nothing to do with it."

"It doesn't?" I couldn't believe it was him saying this to me!

"No, not at all. Jackie and I have a wonderful relationship because she gives me what I want."

"Is that what they call it these days? Is that the way it goes?"

"That's the way it goes."

He really knew how to rub it in, the bastard.

"All right, Jerry," I said, and started to walk away. He put a hand on my arm. Oh, he knew all the tricks. He was a master.

"You know, Nina, you're getting older so you'd better start realizing what life is all about. When you're going with a guy, you just can't hold hands and expect him to be satisfied. You're too old for carrying school books."

"Don't worry, Jerry," I said, pulling my arm away. "I'm not carrying school books anymore." And I walked away, sure that I had had the last word, poor jerk.

Christmas Eve came. Billie and I had a tree in our apartment. There was a big family dinner at my mother's with the whole family all together, like always, and we exchanged gifts and got around the piano and sang carols. The bill at the Tropicana closed on New Year's Eve and after the last show the management threw a party for the cast. The star stayed around long enough to wish everybody a Happy New Year and we all drank champagne and kissed each other the way only show people can without meaning anything by it. Right in the middle of all the kissing and hugging, Jerry and I came face to face.

"Well, it's been nice working with you," I said.

"It's been nice working with you, Nina."

I had about three glasses of bubbly in me so I couldn't let well enough alone.

"I just want you to know something, Jerry. This experience has been great. I must say, I certainly learned a lot about life and especially from you."

He looked bored, like I was too much and he didn't want any more.

"Nina, you better start growing up. I'm talking to you like a friend now. You're living in a glass bubble. Life just isn't the way you think it is."

"OK, OK."

"Anyhow, Happy New Year," and he kissed me on the cheek.

"Thank you, the same to you."

Let him go, Nina. Let him go!

"I suppose you'll be bringing in the New Year with your new-found love."

Gone!

He walked back to me, and standing very close he said, "I'd like to bring in the New Year with you."

For a minute I didn't think I had heard him right.

"I'd really like to bring in the New Year with you."

I held my breath for a minute.

Well, Nina, I said to myself, if this is the way to hold him, why not?

"In half an hour? My apartment?"

"Sure your girlfriend isn't sick or something?"

"It so happens Billie is out of town." He got my back up a little with that crack, but it happened to be the truth. At that very moment Billie was whooping it up on a cruise ship somewhere in the Caribbean. Billie, who was a comedienne, was no Lucille Ball, and jobs were hard to come by for her, so when she was offered this job two days after Christmas with this cruise line entertainment staff, she grabbed it even though the pay was lousy.

"I hate to leave you feeling the way you do," she said, the morning she picked up her suitcase and headed for the door. "Just play it cool, honey, and try not to be alone on New Year's Eve. Be with someone . . . anyone . . . preferably a man."

Well, I was certainly taking her advice, but if she knew how, she would have swum all the way back to stop me.

Everybody was too busy drinking and kissing to notice me leaving. I got back to the apartment via cab, took a fast shower, put on one of Billie's nightgowns—orange see-through, if you please used some toilet water and perfume, and sat down in the living room to wait for Jerry. There was some scotch left in a bottle that Billie kept for social occasions. I was so shivery and nervous, I felt I needed something, so I poured some over a couple of rocks and sat on the edge of the sofa, my eyes on the front door, waiting for the bell to ring.

All right, go ahead and laugh. It's funny, isn't it, really funny . . . an eighteen-year-old virgin . . . excuse me, an eighteen-and-a-half-year-old virgin . . . sitting around in a sexy nightie waiting for her knight in shining armor to come charging in and hop into bed with her. Don't you think it's funny? I do, but then you know me, I'm all mixed up, right?

What was I expecting? Well, as I said before, I had very romantic ideas about sex in those days and about men in general. I expected Jerry to come in, have a drink with me, sit with me on the sofa with his arm around me, kiss me, neck with me a little, very passionate but gentle necking, then when I was ready to melt away with desire, whatever that meant, pick me up in his arms, carry me into the bedroom, put me on the bed, take off my nightgown, and shower me with kisses on my face, my neck, my shoulders, my arms . . . I think my imagination stopped there. I don't think I knew that men kissed any further down.

When the bell rang, I jumped so I almost spilled my scotch all over Billie's nightgown. I stood there for a minute without moving. The bell rang again.

Look, Nina baby, I said to myself, you're going to go through with this. You are going to do it because this is the way to hold this man. After all, didn't you come to New York to live? Well, now's the time to start living.

I opened the door and Jerry walked in. I kissed him and he kissed me back, not very passionately, just an ordinary kiss.

"How about a drink to toast the New Year?" I said.

"No, no," he said. "Come over here." And, putting an arm around me, he started walking me into the bedroom. He didn't waste any time. There was enough light coming in from the living room for me to see that he was taking off his pants.

"Can't we talk a while?" I said. "You know, you're making this very cut and dried and I'm still kind of nervous."

"There's nothing to be nervous about. Come on, baby, I want to make love to you very badly."

"Well, you know I'm very inexperienced, so forgive me, but at this point, I'm really quite confused. I mean, is this the way—?"

"You're not backing out on me, are you?"

"Well, we're here, aren't we? And we're talking about it, and . . ."

"Yeah, well I didn't come here to talk about it. Come on, let's get into bed."

I lay down on the bed and he lay down next to me. I was very rigid and so nervous I was trembling all over. He turned to me, pulled up my nightgown, right up to my neck and looked down at me. I don't know how much he could see in the dim light but I guess it was enough, because the next thing I knew he was kissing my face and my neck and shoulders and squeezing my breasts in his hands.

I said to myself, this isn't so bad, because it was a little like what I had imagined, but then his kisses turned to a kind of sucking, like he was trying to grab pieces of my flesh in his mouth and suck them dry. His head slid down to my breasts and he began chewing on my nipples with his lips, squeezing them hard and pulling at them and even biting them with his teeth. It hurt like hell and I tried to push his head away, but he kept right on. His breath was coming in gasps because he was trying to breathe at the same time that he was trying to eat me or whatever he was doing, and God, it was horrible!

Then he rolled completely over on me and I felt one of his knees between my thighs, forcing them apart. He lifted himself and used his hands to push them apart wider. Then he was in between my legs and I could feel something poking me just below my belly button. One of his hands pushed in between our bodies and I felt the something slide down between my hairs and then it was something round and rubbery against me and a pain shot up through my middle from inside my vagina and right into my guts. I closed my eyes and put my head back and tried not to cry out.

Jesus, God, am I supposed to enjoy this? I thought to myself. At that point, I wanted to call the whole thing off but I figured that if I showed him I wasn't enjoying it he would get mad. On the other hand, if I did seem to enjoy it he would think I had had some sexual experience before and all that line about being a virgin was just a way of teasing him, so I shut up like the jerk I was. I clenched my teeth and breathed hard through my nose the way you do in the dentist's chair when he's drilling.

That's what Jerry was doing. He was drilling, pushing that thing of his in me and grinding away at me like he was trying to put a hole through me all the way up to my head. I must have been very tight because he was rubbing me raw and sore. His whole body was on me like a dead weight and he was panting harder than ever. I opened my eyes and looked up into his face. I wanted to say, Jerry, what is this? What's the matter with you? What are you doing to me? I love you, don't you understand? But his eyes were closed and his lips were pulled back showing his teeth like he was a dog snarling at a piece of meat, and I knew I couldn't get through to him. Then his mouth opened and his jaw dropped and he looked like a little boy being surprised.

"Ah! Ah! Ah! Ah!" he said and kept saying it, and inside me I could feel his thing bumping and jerking around while he kept it pressed in hard as he could. Then it was over. His head fell forward with his mouth open against the side of my neck, his body stopped jerking, and he lay still. The insides of my thighs ached. I tried to push

31

him off but he wouldn't budge. I started to cry. I pushed a hand into my mouth so he wouldn't hear me and turned my face away so he couldn't see the tears. Why? What the hell was I protecting him from? Why did I hide the tears? Was I trying to save the bastard from feeling guilty? Why the hell didn't I let the prick see my crying so he'd know! Let him feel guilty! Let him lose a night's sleep! God, if I had my way he never would have slept again as long as he lived for what he did to me! Or balled another woman!

He moved. He lifted his head and the weight was lifted from me and he got off. I opened my wet eyes and looked up at him. He had his back to me, heading for the bathroom. I heard the paper roll rattle and then there was a splashing sound in the bowl that went on for a long time. That was the first time I ever heard a man urinate. It was a sound that got to be very familiar to me. I got used to how they always head for the john when they're through. It's a wonder they don't sit down and have a good shit while they're at it. That would really empty them out all the way around.

Jerry came back into the bedroom and pulled on his pants.

"I got to run. Call you in the morning," and he was gone. I heard the front door open and close behind him. I looked at the alarm clock on the night table. It was a quarter past four on the morning of the first day of the new year. The whole thing had taken maybe twenty minutes. The only thing he didn't do was leave money on the bed.

Chapter
FOUR

For the next three hours I lay on the bed and cried. I couldn't stop. Not because I wasn't a virgin anymore. That didn't bother me. I had always known, even if I refused to admit it to myself, that I couldn't go along in show business and expect to remain a virgin until I was married, whenever that would be. It just couldn't happen that way, not in a thousand years. Anyhow, at the rate I was going I was too damn curious to remain a virgin, and now I wasn't curious anymore, so what the hell.

I cried for Jerry. I just couldn't get it through my head that this was the same person who had been so nice to my mother and taken her out and who was so kind and gentle and understanding when we first met and was really sympathetic about how I felt about life and could kiss me with such tenderness and feeling. But it was done, and I'd been had; that's how I felt. I had had my first real experience with a man, so now I could walk around with that knowing look in my eyes and not be embarrassed at all those virgin jokes people were always telling whenever I was around. Now I knew what it was all about. I also knew what men were all about, too, or so I thought. I didn't know how much I still had to learn. In fact, you could have filled an entire library with what I didn't know about sex.

You're going to hear a lot about my life until Herbie stops buying me these tapes, so you might as well get used to it. When I was a kid, my father dominated my life, the way he dominated all our lives during those years. My days went according to how he felt. If he felt good, I felt good. If he was bothered about something, I was bothered. When he got mad, I stayed out of his way, because he had a vicious, vicious temper which he would take out on my mother and us kids. On those days I was afraid.

I never had what you would call a normal childhood. I couldn't play out in the street with the other kids on the block because I might fall and scrape my knees, and how would that look when I was onstage singing with my sisters? And I couldn't go to Coney Island and go on the rides because I might scream and hurt my voice. I couldn't do a lot of the things kids my age were doing, so I never really had the chance to get to meet boys the way most girls do.

When I was a kid we never spoke about sex in my family. Sex in an Italian family? At that time? Forget it, Charlie! I'm talking about the old-fashioned Italian families where the parents were born in the old country and came here when they were young. All they knew about bringing up kids was the way they had been brought up, and in their families the girls were always brought up strict, right? And we were four girls, so you can imagine! We were the most strictly brought up kids you ever saw, not only because we were girls but also because we were in show business. When Dad took us out of town to play dates, he would make us stay in the dressing room before and after we went on. Then he would take us back to our hotel room and lock us in, while he went out to have a few drinks with the boys. Or with the girls, as the case might be, as I later found out.

In our family the things that went on between men and women were so shameful and disgusting they couldn't be talked about. Girls especially had to be protected. Would you believe that when my older sisters went to parties, as they were allowed to once in a while when there was a wedding or an engagement in the neighborhood, they never danced with the boys because my father had told them that was how a girl got pregnant!

"Boys are only after one thing!"

What the one thing was he never explained. I guess it was supposed to be understood that the one thing was dirty and that was all the explanation we needed.

By the time I was twelve, I was completely ignorant about my own body. I hardly knew what it looked like. Or anybody else's, including my sisters'. At home, we never got undressed in front of each other. I knew that my sisters had breasts which I didn't have at the time even though I never saw them, because as the younger girls got older I'd hear my mother tell my father that Dolores or Marcie needed a training bra. But I never saw my sisters in their bras or even their slips. Not once. We would all get dressed and undressed in the bathroom. In dressing rooms, we all wore big, loose dressing gowns and we made our changes under them. We would slip a hand inside and unhook one side and then the other and then wiggle and squirm to get at the back and then slip it out or down or around or what-not. Would you believe it? You had to be almost double-jointed!

No one ever told me about my monthly, not even my mother, or my sisters, and I guess I never noticed when they had theirs because they hid it too well. I remember what a shock it was the first time it happened to me. I must have been about twelve. We were at a rehearsal for the Frank Ellis show. It was about four hours before air time and we were all in the dressing room getting ready for the runthrough when all of a sudden I saw this red stain on my dress. Was I scared! I thought I was dying. Angie saw it and got all red in the face, but I could see that she was trying hard not to notice. Dolores was too busy fussing with her dress and Marcie just looked helpless, like she wanted to help but didn't know how.

I started to cry and one of the other girls on the show who was there at the time, a script girl or something, took

34

me to the network medical department where the nurse took care of me. I'll never forget it. The nurse said to me, "Why, honey, you've become a young woman!" She took off my dress and had it washed. Then she found me a Modess and sent out for a belt and showed me how to put it on and told me what was happening. That was my first and only sex lesson and it had to come from a total stranger. The rest I learned as I went along.

For instance, I used to see a lot of things going on backstage at the theaters we played, like the comedian who always had some kind of broad in his dressing room between shows. I remember once saying to my sisters, "That girl singer's been in Georgie's dressing room for over an hour. What are they doing in there so long?" And Dolores giggling and Angie and Marcie saying, "Shut up, Dolores!" very stern, and then breaking down and laughing themselves. Later on, when I was seventeen and dating, it wasn't just ice cream sodas between me and the boys I dated, but that was later on.

Being in show business, I'd been around, and I was very arrogant and sure of myself. I was the youngest and therefore the cutest of the four, because the youngest is always the cutest, right? Everybody always made a fuss over me and paid me a lot of attention, so by the time I was twelve I had what you might call a very strong personality of my own. Besides, most of our routines were built around my voice because I had that brassy quality that gave us our sound. It really cut the grease, and most of the time it was me carrying the melody with my sisters supplying the doo-doo-doos behind me.

At twelve, I was the most outspoken, gutsiest one of the four. Frank Ellis nicknamed me "Grandma" the first time he met us. Frank had had a radio show on network since the Year One. He was a very funny guy and a famous comedian, and his Ellisville characters and the way he would take off on network executives and big shots in general had people listening in from coast to coast every Sunday night. We auditioned for him wearing dollar dresses my mother had bought, marked down from two ninety-eight to ninety-nine cents. All these men were sitting there staring at us with their fancy tweed jackets and their important faces and all I could think of was, Did my mother remember to take off the price tags?

Frank listened and he liked us, and then he said in that funny voice of his, talking through his nose like he did, "Where's your dad? I'd like to talk to him about having

35

you kids on the show." Dad was home sick that night. He was always kind of sickly with a bad liver or with piles or his stomach, and at that time he was sick so much he hardly ever went with us anymore. We looked at each other, not knowing what to say, so I piped up with, "He's home in Brooklyn."

"What's his phone number? I want to talk to him right away."

I didn't want Frank to know that we were too poor to have a phone, so I said, "He's busy. I don't think you can reach him by phone right now, but that's all right. I'll tell him all about it when we get home. What's the deal?"

He looked at me and grinned his famous grin and said, "Oh, so you're the Grandma of the act." And everybody laughed because I was the youngest and smallest, but the name stuck, and I guess it fit because I always seemed to be the one running the act. I was only ten when we went on radio, so imagine what I was like at twelve. By the time I was twelve I was picking out all the shoes and dresses we wore, and after Dad died I took over as manager of the act, and I really got to learn my way around in the business. I always knew when a club owner was trying to pull a fast one on us and I knew how to take care of him, too. I also knew how to handle the star of the show when he tried to cut our time out front because he felt we were getting too much applause. And if the orchestra tried to speed us up during rehearsals, I was the one who told the leader, "You better play in our tempo; otherwise we'll be a beat behind." With me there were no ands, ifs, or buts. It was my way or else.

By twelve I had spent more nights in Pullman berths, eaten more meals in lousy restaurants, and seen more towns in the U.S.A. than most people do in their entire lives. By the time I was fourteen, I was really an adult except when it came to being experienced with the opposite sex. And yet if one of my older sisters got involved with some jerkoff and didn't know how to get rid of him, guess who did it for her? Right. Grandma.

When I was fourteen, Angie got mixed up with this jerkoff who said he had only been married once. I found out from someone who knew him very well that he had actually been to the altar four times. Angie tried to drop him but he was very obnoxious and kept hanging around. He used to drive out to the house in Brooklyn and park in front, waiting for her to come out. Finally, one day I called him up on the phone and told him to lay off.

"I know all about you," I told him. "All about how many times you've been married and how many kids you've got, too. So don't come around here anymore. Leave my sister alone; otherwise, I'm going to blow the whistle on you. There won't be a chorus girl or singer or club owner or theater manager from New York to Frisco that won't know all about you. So lay off."

He listened, and he laid off. He really did. Of course, over the phone he couldn't tell which sister he was talking to, but can you imagine a fourteen-year-old girl talking like that to an older man?

At seventeen, I started to notice that the dancer on the bill in Boston was pretty cute, the boy singer in Cleveland was adorable, the acrobat in Youngstown was gorgeous. I started sneaking out to meet them when my sisters weren't looking, or when I thought they weren't looking, because after Dad died my older sisters looked out for me. They thought they knew what I was doing, and they never made much fuss about it as long as I had my ice cream soda with the boy and got back in time for the next show, but they didn't know about the necking.

We'd sit on a park bench if a park was handy, or they'd see me back to my hotel room. Of course I was sharing the room with my sisters so they couldn't come in, but we used to stand in the hall or duck into the stairway landing behind the fire door and neck on the stairs until we heard someone coming. It was mostly kissing, kissing, kissing, until the boy got too excited and started using his hands. Then I would turn it off and run for home. In other words, it wasn't until I was seventeen that I finally got into the normal kind of boy-girl relationship which most girls start at fourteen or fifteen.

By eighteen you might say that I was considerably behind when it came to knowing about sex and men, especially when you see how much the kids of eighteen know today, but in my family, as far as my mother and sisters were concerned, that was the way it should be.

When I said to my mother right out of a clear blue sky one day, "You know, Mom, I'll be eighteen next month. I'd like to get my own apartment in New York," you can imagine how she took it. Angelina and Marcella, the two eldest, were married, but Dolores and I were living with her whenever we weren't traveling and I was still her baby.

When she recovered from the shock, she said, "How can you do this to me, Nina? Just because a couple of your sisters went off and got married?"

"But, Mom, I'm not going off to get married. I have this girlfriend who's a comedienne—I told you about Billie Adelle—and she and I figured out that we could share her apartment and live cheaper than one. Besides, I'd like to meet more people on my own."

She looked at me like she was trying to see inside my head and already knew what she would find there.

"I suppose you mean boys."

"Well, yes, boys, girls, friends. And I would also like to see what life is really all about. I've had pinches of it so far, just pinches. Now I would like to taste the full ingredients."

"I hope it doesn't give you indigestion," she said, and that was that. The next week I moved in with Billie, not exactly with Mom's blessings but at least she didn't fight it. Angie and Marcie made more fuss about it than she did, but I was growing up and I had a right to my own life, so what could they say, right?

So there I was, living with my girlfriend Billie in an apartment hotel on West Eighty-sixth Street. We really thought we were big time. We only had three furnished rooms, but we had room service running up and down like we were in the royal suite at the Plaza. The bellhops didn't mind. Every time we picked up the phone, we had four jerkoffs in hot pants knocking at the door, every one of them trying to make out with the two chicks in 8F.

It lasted all of six weeks, and then I had to louse it up by falling for Jerry, but those six weeks were great because up till then that was the only time I ever had in my whole life really to myself. I couldn't get enough of doing what I pleased when I pleased without having to tell anyone where I was going and why. Of course, I had rehearsals because we were singing at the Latin Quarter then, but the rest of the time it was just me, or Billie and me, living it up in the big city. We walked all over Manhattan looking at the sights by day, and since I was dating a lot, I got to see the sights at night, too. I never had trouble finding men to take me out. Almost every young male performer in New York was after me. It was really more than I could handle and it must have gone to my head, all those beautiful young guys practically lining up to take me out, because look what a stupid broad I was with Jerry. I didn't realize then that all they were after was my cherry. Me being a virgin must have been the biggest joke in the business, but I was too dumb to see it. All that those guys wanted was to get me into bed so one of them could

38

brag to his friends how he had been the first with the well-known Nina Brandi—and some of them weren't that young either.

Freddie Manners, for instance, of Manners and Allen. They were a comedy team, very successful and popular in the movies and in vaudeville. Freddie was the slapstick comic part of the act. He was a little under medium height, kind of stout and with a big mouth, which was his trademark. When he was stuck for an answer he used to open his mouth all the way so he looked like the Grand Canyon; then he'd realize he didn't have the answer and close it and look sad. Dorey Allen was more good-looking and he could sing, too. Freddie would always get into trouble and start yelling for Dorey to bail him out.

"Dorey," he used to call in a funny, deep, dumb-sounding voice like Archie's on "Duffy's Tavern." "Dorey! Duh . . . uh . . . help, Dorey!"

And when Dorey showed up he would make matters worse and then the two of them would be in hot water. They were very big box office before they split up.

Pumpkin. That's what Freddie always called me. "Hi-ya, pumpkin," he would say in that funny voice, and pat me on the head and chuck me under the chin. That's when I was younger. When we were playing the Tropicana with them, he tried a couple of funny things that I didn't fully understand at the time but that are clear as glass now.

For instance, there was a hotel next to the Tropicana on Forty-eighth Street called the Carlisle. The Tropicana only had a dressing room for the chorus line, so the management used to take rooms in the Carlisle so the talent didn't have to go all the way back to their own apartments or hotels between shows to rest up and change. When Manners and Allen played the Tropicana, they each had a suite at the Carlisle because of all their arrangers and gofers and hangers-on.

One day I had just finished changing at the Carlisle and was on my way to meet Jerry when one of Freddie's gofers, one of those guys who are always hanging around celebrities so that they can go for coffee and cigarettes and things, catches me in the lobby and tells me that Freddie wants to see me in his suite. So up I went to Freddie's suite and there he is with his usual cast of characters hanging around.

"Hiya, pumpkin," he said. "How are you?"

"Fine, just fine," I said.

39

"Come sit down with me, pumpkin. I want to talk to you . . . no, over here next to me." So I sat next to him on the couch and he put his arm around me and cuddled me and talked. Mostly he talked about me seeing Jerry Miller and how so many people were talking about it and things like that. I just listened. I didn't say much. Many people in the business treated me like a kid. They always remembered me as I was at ten years old on the Frank Ellis show, the littlest Brandi, always up front, so cute with the dark bangs and the big black eyes and the big brassy voice. To some of these people, I will always be ten years old. I guess it helps them hang on to their youth.

Not Freddie Manners. He had other ideas, but after talking to me for a while and squeezing and hugging me, he finally let me go. A week later, he and Dorey were asked to do a benefit at the Commodore and he asked the Brandi Sisters to join him on the bill. We wouldn't get paid, of course, but it was a big honor to be on the same bill with Manners and Allen so, of course, our manager accepted and we went along.

The night of the benefit, Freddie called our apartment in the Carlisle—we were doing the benefit between shows at the Tropicana—and said he was going to drive us to the Commodore so we would all arrive together. After the first show, we all piled into Freddie's car, the four of us and his musical director. Freddie was driving his own Lincoln Continental, the famous Lincoln that was always getting written up in the columns, the one with the policeman's whistle on the outside that Freddie loved to sound by pressing a special button on the steering wheel. He had already gotten three tickets for sounding it in New York, but a little thing like a traffic ticket or even three never stopped Freddie from doing what he wanted to do in that Lincoln. When he was really looped, he used to drive all over Los Angeles sounding the whistle and driving the cops wild, but that was L.A., not New York.

All the way to the Commodore, Freddie was very quiet. Usually before a show he gags it up, which is his way of warming up before going on, but this time there wasn't a peep out of him and he didn't sound the whistle once. The music man was up front with my sister Angie between him and Freddie. The rest of us were in the back. When we stopped at the Commodore and started to get out I leaned forward and put my hand on Freddie's shoulder. I was going to say something funny about his not sounding the whistle. He turned around to see whose hand was on his shoulder, saw that it was mine and pulled back like I had the measles.

"Get the fuck away from me!" he yelled.

"What!" I was amazed.

He picked up my hand where it was resting on the back of the seat and tried to throw it in my face, like it was a glove instead of a hand.

"I said, get the fuck away from me!"

All I could say was, "What did I do?"

"Don't you ever get in the same car with me and sit in back!" he said, and he got out and slammed the door.

He didn't talk to me for a full week after that. Then I guess he decided to give me a second chance. Now, I'm talking about a guy who is seen every day with as many as six or eight different broads and has the reputation of banging them all before the day is over. The night the show closed at the Tropicana, he had me up to his suite again. To say good-bye, he said. This time he gave me a soul kiss right in front of all his people.

"Stay a while," he said, trying to make his funny voice deep and passionate.

"Oh, never!" I said, backing away from him. "Bye, now! My sisters are calling me! See you!"

Freddie never forgave me for that. But never! Every time I ran into him after that, he showed what a grudge he carried for me.

Well, none of the guys made it with me, not even Freddie Manners, but maybe I would have been better off if one of the young guys had. At least I wouldn't have gotten myself all involved and messed up with an expert cocksman like Jerry Miller, the bastard.

Chapter
FIVE

All day New Year's Day I lay by the phone waiting for it to ring. Jerry didn't call the next day, either, or the day after that, or that week or the next week. Billie came back with a terrific tan, and when she heard my story, the first thing she wanted to know was did he use a rubber. I couldn't say yes or no because I wasn't watching him while he was getting ready to bang me, and I wouldn't have been able to tell the difference anyhow, so that got me all worried and upset worse than before. I sweated out my next monthly which came right on time, thank God, so I was off that hook, but I wasn't off Jerry's hook. That took time.

It was weeks before I started going out again. I only left the apartment to go to rehearsals and performances, and in between I moped around, going over and over in my mind how I had been taken and used. Billie said Jerry had acted like he was in a cathouse, and when she told me what a cathouse was I agreed with her and hated the sonofabitch more than ever for treating me like a common, ordinary hooker. I was also disgusted with myself because I felt dirty and degraded, and I couldn't understand how with my background and upbringing I could have let myself be dragged down that way.

Most of all I was hurt and angry, because, after all, I had poured all my emotions into Jerry for so long and look how he had treated me. He was the one I sent cards to every day when he was out of town. He was the guy who had me stuffing quarters into the phone in between shows so I could hear his voice for a few minutes, the one I bought the little gifts for that said, Hello-again-I-still-love-you when he came back, and all I got for it was humiliation and shame. But you want to know something? You probably won't believe this, or you'll think I'm nuts or something, but in spite of all that, deep down inside I was really hoping that he would call and say he was sorry and ask me to forgive him. Which of course he never did. I know it sounds crazy, but that was the way I felt, would you believe it?

Finally I decided that he had gotten what he wanted from me and I was no good to him anymore and that was that, so I started dating again, first with one guy and then with another, and gradually I got myself back to normal. At first I held all my dates off at arm's length. I was willing to go out with them and have a good time but I wouldn't go any further. My evenings ended at the front door of the hotel and that was that. Then I started to study these guys. I listened closely to what they were saying to me, and little by little I began to realize that I could read between the lines and see what they were after. They would tell me how cute I was, how great I sang, how great the Brandi Sisters were, how adorable I was, how wonderful it was to come from a big Italian family, all that crap, but you know what it all added up

42

to? You know where it was all supposed to lead? To bed. Where else? That was the whole bit with them. Make it in the kip.

"Hi, sweetheart, when's your roommate coming back?"

I swear, that was all they had on their minds. So, I decided, what the hell, this sex bit was supposed to be the greatest thing going for everybody, women as well as men, right, so why not climb on board for the joyride. When you've been to bed with one guy, you'd be surprised how easy it is to go to bed with the next one, and the next, and the one after that. At first I didn't get a hell of a lot out of it, but after a while I began to like it in a way, especially if I was in bed with some jerkoff who didn't mind if I acted just as animalistic as he did. In fact, some of them really loved it when I tore loose and climbed on top instead of lying back waiting for them to supply the action. They never seemed to understand that I was trying to ball them instead of the other way around, which of course I knew I really couldn't do, but it made me feel good to try, anyhow.

The one thing I made sure of was that I didn't get emotionally involved. I had been that route already and look what it got me. Anyhow, I didn't know it then but I was still torching for Jerry. I found that out about six months later, in Miami. We were singing at the Saxony and I walked into the lounge one night after the last show to meet some friends, and guess who's sitting there watching my entrance? Right. The Great Cherry-Picker himself.

I knew he was on the bill at the Surfer, so I really wasn't too surprised. In fact I had been telling myself all week just how I was going to act when and if I ran into him, which I was sure was bound to happen, but seeing him there without any warning caught me off guard.

"Hi," he says, standing in front of me so I can't get by.

"Oh, hello."

I wanted to walk on, but all of a sudden my knees started to shake and I had to stand still for a minute to get control of myself.

"How are you doing?"

"Fine, thank you. Will you excuse me, please? Some friends are waiting for me."

I tried to pass but he took me by the arm.

"Never mind your friends. You're with me tonight."

"Oh, really!"

I tried to get back to my prepared script but there was a threat in his voice that made me forget my lines.

"That's right, and believe me, you're not going to be with anybody else."

I tried to look him right in the eye so he could see it wouldn't work but he was looking right back and a look passed between us that was like a challenge. All right, I said to myself, let's see what happens. I'm not the naïve kid I was six months ago. I've had a few affairs myself. This time I'm not going to lie back and just let him have a field day with me. You see, there wasn't the slightest doubt in my mind right that minute that I would go to bed with him.

I left my friends waiting for me and went with Jerry to his hotel. There was no drink before, no explanations, or anything leading up to it. There wasn't any real emotion in the scene, either, just a lot of choreography. When he kissed me, I kissed him back just as hard. When he put his tongue in my mouth, I sucked it and pushed mine against it and made him take mine in his. When he used his hands on me, I used my hands on him, driving him crazy stroking and rubbing and tickling. And when he tried to roll over on me and give me the knee and just push in, I made him wait until I was good and ready, and then I took him in. And when he was in, I didn't let him out until I was through. I locked my legs around his hips and my arms around his neck and I rode that pole of his until I squeezed all there was to squeeze out of myself and out of him. And when I finally stopped grinding my ass, he didn't pull out on his own, he fell out like a wet rag and lay back.

There, you fucking sonofabitch, I thought to myself, now we're even. But when I looked at him he had that little boy's look on his face, surprised and pleased, and I knew I hadn't won a thing, that I couldn't ever punish him that way. Then he opened his eyes and looked at me and put out his arms and I fell into them. Sleeping and fucking, we were in each other's arms all night, and when we woke up it was daylight and I knew that I was just as much in love with him as ever and there wasn't anything I could do about it.

We stayed together for a week, and in that week I went from heaven to hell and back again every day. He told me that I had held back too long and teased him too much and that was why he had practically raped me the first time. He told me he was sterile and couldn't have kids,

44

but by that time I had met another girl who had slept with him and she had had two abortions. He told me that he couldn't settle down because it wasn't in him, that's why he was getting divorced, but that I was his best girl, if I wanted to be. All the things that can tear a woman's heart to pieces, he told me, and then at night he put the pieces back together again in bed, because as the week went on, it wasn't just choreography anymore, not for me.

My sisters didn't care at all for what was going on because it was obvious that I was spending more time at Jerry's hotel than anywhere else. We'd finish the last show each night at the Saxony and then I would disappear and not show up until the next evening in time for makeup or for a rehearsal, if there was one. For a long time now, I had been building up quite a reputation with the columnists and people in the business. It was almost like a lottery, trying to guess who Nina Brandi was going to be seen with next. Angie and Marcie both had spoken to me about it, and Dolores used to make all kind of snotty remarks every time we got into another town to play a date, things like "Who's it going to be in this town, Nina?" This time I told Angie that Jerry Miller was *the* man in my life and I wasn't going to give him up just because my sisters didn't approve and I guess she was wise enough to see that nothing she could say would matter anyhow, so she stopped pushing me and she got the others to lay off, too.

Saturday morning, at the end of that wonderful week, the phone rang while we were still in bed, and it was Jerry's father. He had just blown into town for a week of sun and sand. We had plans to spend the day on the beach but Jerry was very close to his old man and he couldn't brush him off so he asked me to meet him and his dad for cocktails at five. He would spend the day with the old boy and I would get some shopping done and then we could meet at the Saxony and have dinner there and Jerry's father could see his son's girl do her stuff. That's how he referred to me now, as his girl. Need I say I loved it?

I had a nice day doing the stores and buying a few things and then I went back to the hotel. I was just crossing the lobby to the elevators, figuring I still had time for a shower before meeting Miller and Son, when somebody called my name. I turned around and there was Jimmy Jones, an old friend from way back. Jimmy was a singer who was coming up then and creating an awful lot of noise, as they say in the business. He was just about to open at the Breakwater. Jimmy and I had always been great friends since the first time we played a bill together in Vegas, so we had a happy little reunion going there for a while. We went into the lounge and found a table off in a corner and started talking. We hadn't seen each other for a long time and we asked each other a lot of questions and got a lot of answers about people we both knew. And of course we talked about his nose, because the first thing I had noticed was that it was fixed. Some time back, Jimmy had had some kind of accident in which his nose was broken very badly. Not only his nose but a lot of the bones in his face, too. Nobody knows to this day just what kind of accident it was, and in spite of a lot of rumors, including one about his being beaten up by a bookie, no one who knows Jimmy real well ever asks him, out of respect. The break had been so bad and his face was so messed up that he had been told he had to wait a long time before it would heal completely so he could have it fixed. Now, most guys I know, if that happened to them, would have retired into a dark room and stayed there until they could get to a plastic surgeon. Not Jimmy. As soon as he looked pretty decent again, he got back in front of audiences and he made that broken schnozz of his into a trademark. He took his misfortune and built it up into an asset, and the nose plus his wonderful personality really gave him a terrific image.

Anyhow, there he was with his nose all fixed again. He had finally been to a plastic surgeon who had made it as good as new. Nobody had known about it, because Jimmy and his manager had kept it hushed up, and that night Jimmy was going on in front of an audience for the first time with his face made over. Naturally, he was kind of nervous about it. He had had the broken schnozz for so long and made so many jokes about it that it had become like a favorite prop. And now, here he was going on without it. I told him he looked great and that I knew he was going to be a big hit, which he was, and he dug that so much that he leaned over and gave me a big kiss and a hug. Then he had to run, and I remembered my date, so we broke it up. As I was walking through the lounge to the lobby, I thought I saw Jerry. He was with an older man in a new straw hat and wearing a Hollywood sport shirt, very loud and splashy, and they were walking out ahead of me very fast. I called after them but they didn't seem to hear and kept right on walking. When I got to the lobby they were gone. Then I checked my watch and saw that it wasn't quite five yet, so I figured maybe my watch was fast and that I had made a mistake and that wasn't them. I went up to my room, showered very fast and changed, and got back down to the lounge inside a half hour. By this time it was after five and they still weren't there. I sat down and waited for a while but they never showed up. Finally I wandered over to the dining room, thinking maybe they were waiting for me at a table because we were supposed to have dinner together, but there was no sign of them there either.

I didn't see or hear from Jerry all that evening, and though I was a little annoyed about being stood up for dinner, I thought that maybe his father wasn't feeling well or something and Jerry would be in touch when he could. After the first show, I went out to the front desk to see if there were any messages for me, and there was Jerry looking as though he'd been waiting.

"I want to speak to you alone," he said, sounding very serious. "It's urgent and private."

I knew there'd be no one in the dressing rooms between shows, so we went there. He closed the door behind us, and then he turned to me and said, "You know, I want to tell you something. I always knew that you were a cheap broad but I never knew you could be that cheap."

How is that for openers! For a minute I was really rocked back on my heels. I couldn't think of anything to say but "What?" He looked very angry and upset, and I could see that he wasn't joking. So I thought to myself, something was very wrong and I'd better get to the bottom of it right away.

"Jerry, what's wrong? What's the matter?"

I think I started to put a hand on his arm because he moved back and away like he didn't want me to touch him.

"What's wrong?" he almost spat the words out. "My father comes to town and I tell him all about you, about my girl, and he wants to meet you and we walk in and there you are making it with a spade."

I looked at him, trying to understand what he was saying, and then it started to sink in. He must have seen Jimmy Jones give me that hug and kiss, and Jimmy happens to be black. Now I'm no big brain when it comes to politics or race questions or things like that, but to me the color of a man's skin never meant very much. If he was a good joe, or a great performer, that was all that mattered. I hadn't ever made it with anybody black, but I

47

knew lots of black entertainers and I was always very friendly with them, and sex just never came into the picture.

"But Jimmy's just a good friend," I said. "We've never been to bed and we never will."

"Why should I believe that? Hell, you've been running around with everything else, so what's the difference! What's a colored guy, more or less? There's no difference, is there? Or are you just curious enough to find out for yourself?"

"Jerry, you've got it wrong!"

"I don't think so!"

He meant it. I started to boil inside. I can take just so much and then the old Sicilian temper starts boiling up and then, brother, watch out! After all, this was coming from Jerry Miller, the guy who had treated me like a two-bit whore just a few months back. And he hadn't even had the decency to try to make it up. He had just walked back into my life and bed, and now here he was sounding off like the purest lily in the field. It was too much.

"Get out of this dressing room," I told him. "Right now. And do me a favor. Don't ever call me. Forget my name. Forget that you ever knew me, because we're through."

"You're telling me!"

"We should have been through after that first night!"

"Here we go again. You and your first night. You know what the trouble with you is? You're a romanticist!"

"And your trouble is you don't know how to be a decent human being. Jimmy Jones is a wonderful guy and a great human being, which is something you'll never be as long as you live."

"You've got an awful lot of waking up to do before you finally realize what it's all about."

"Thanks for the two-bit philosophy, Mr. Anthony. Coming from a two-bit comic, you can just bet I'm going to write it down in my scrapbook and treasure it for life. Now would you please get out of my life so I can start straightening out and get back to normal!"

"You'll never straighten out. You're too screwed up."

"Maybe I am. But I'm still going to start over again and fall in love the right way and get married, too."

He laughed.

"You'll never love anybody but me," he said. "You're a cheap broad and you like to be treated the way I treated you and you'll never be able to love a decent guy as long as you live."

I walked to the door and opened it.

"I've had just about enough of this conversation," I told him, shaking all over and hanging on to the doorknob behind my back for support. "You think whatever you want. Just leave me alone. And tell your father I deeply apologize because I'm sorry he's so prejudiced. Tell him that I don't happen to be making it with Jimmy, but if I were, that would be my business, not his or yours or anybody else's, understand? Just my business."

He walked to the door and stood very close to me.

"OK, sweetheart," he said, "but before I go I want to do something I've wanted to do since the first time I met you."

I saw his hand go up in the air, but I didn't duck or try to move away because I didn't believe he would do it. He won't hit me, I thought to myself; he wouldn't do a thing like that. And then his hand slammed across the side of my face and I went flying across the room and down on the floor. I landed on my side and rolled over. My head was ringing like a Chinese gong; the side of my face was on fire; my ear hurt like hell and I couldn't open one eye, but the first thing I did was put my hands to my mouth. All I could think of was my teeth.

I finally got the eye open and the tears started pouring down my face. For a minute I guess I was so stunned I didn't know where I was or what was happening, because with one hand I started feeling around the floor and I knew I was feeling for teeth. You see in my mind I had this picture of my mother sitting on the floor of the kitchen with her apron stained red pressed against her mouth, and the white pieces of bone with the bloody ends lying on the floor in front of her. My father had just knocked out her front teeth. My father had a terrible temper which used to get set off by all kinds of things like his physical complaints, or maybe by his own inner frustrations. And when he blew his stack he would take it out on her and then he would go for us kids.

This one particular time he'd been sitting on a pillow all day because his piles hurt so bad he couldn't walk, and he sent my mother down to Thirteenth Avenue in Boro Park to buy him a shirt. There was one particular shirt he wanted with a certain kind of stripe like the stripe on the end of the Kleenex box at that time. I was about six or seven years old. We were living on the top floor of one of those four-family brick houses you see all over Brooklyn, and I was playing jacks with my sisters on the front porch next to the kitchen, so I saw my mother come back with the shirt and give it to him.

"Julie, I said a narrow stripe, didn't I?"

He moved around on the pillow trying to get in a comfortable position, looking at the shirt like it was a rag or something.

"They don't have a stripe that narrow," my mother said. "This was the only kind they had."

"So why did you buy it?"

"Rosanno, you said you needed a shirt. It's not so wide. You can wear it."

"How can I wear it!" His voice started going up and my mother looked nervous. "With a stripe this wide I'll look like George Raft in a gangster movie. Paul Muni in *Scarface!* Wop, they'll call me. Louis Caruso will take one look at this shirt, he'll call me a wop."

Louis Caruso was an agent who used to get us bookings, and I guess the thought of how Louis Caruso would look at him in that shirt really got to him, because now he got up out of the chair and started to walk up and down with his legs spread apart a little, looking at the shirt and grabbing at his hair.

"But you said you needed a shirt so bad," my poor mother said. "It's not so terrible. It's a nice shirt. It's—"

Then he exploded.

"That's all you know! It's nice! It's not so bad!" He was imitating her now. "It's not nice. And it's bad, yeah it's bad! This is show business I'm in. I got to dress right. I can't take the girls around looking like a wop. Everybody will laugh at me."

He threw the shirt back at her.

"Take it back. Get back the money!"

"It's a discount sale. They don't give back the money. They only exchange."

"Then go back! Exchange it."

"But that's all they got, Rosanno. The shirts, they're all the same. The same stripes."

He grabbed the shirt back and stood there holding it in his hands, waving it around in front of her.

"So what am I gonna do with this?"

My mother just looked at him. Her hands were pulling at her apron and I could see she wanted to turn around and run but she didn't dare to, like when you face a wild animal in a cage you don't dare turn your back. I sat

50

there watching with the ball in my hand. I was frozen and my sisters were frozen, too, just sitting there listening and looking at me because I was the only one who could see what was going on. I saw him pull at the shirt like he wanted to rip it apart. Then he gave a kind of a groan and turned around with his eyes staring and his face all screwed up with pain and rage. There was a pot of spaghetti sauce cooking on the stove and he saw it. He gave a kind of snarl and ran to the stove, lifted the shirt over his head, and slammed it down into the sauce. It landed with a soft splash and sauce splattered out all over him, even on his face. He yelled like he was hurt and put his hands to his face, and my mother ran over to him.

"Rosanno, my God, are you burned?" she cried, trying to make him turn around. He came around slowly, and as he did he put his hands down and I could see the bright red sauce like blood on his face and hands.

"Sure I'm burned," he yelled. "Like this I'm burned," and he hit her across the face with his greasy hands. They made a wet, smacking sound, and he hit her again and again, knocking her back across the kitchen.

"Rosanno, please don't!" my mother screamed, and she covered her face and ran into a corner and crouched down on the floor with him after her, pounding away with his fists.

"Mommamommamommamomma!" Dolores screamed. She ran out of the porch into the kitchen with all the rest of us after her. We all ran through the kitchen and into the other rooms. My sisters ran into the bedroom but I knew better than that. There was no lock on the bedroom door and he could get in there at us, which is what he always did when he got finished beating up my mother. He would pull us out from under the beds one by one, kicking and screaming and pulling at the floor with our hands, and then he would hit us hard as he could until finally he got too tired to hit anymore. I ran into the bathroom because there was a lock on that door, and I locked the door and sat on the floor near the john with my hands over my ears trying not to hear my mother screaming and my sisters being beaten. When it was over, I heard him rush out of the apartment like a wild man. I could hear him groaning and running down the steps and pulling the street door open and then his footsteps fading out in the street as he ran up the block, while out in the hall I could hear the neighbors buzzing and talking and someone saying to call the police. I came out of the

51

bathroom and went into the kitchen. My mother was sitting on the floor with the apron against her mouth. It was turning red and she was staring down at her front teeth on the floor. My beautiful mother. My lovely, gentle, beautiful mother who used to sit by the kitchen window eating a piece of bread sprinkled with sugar for breakfast because that's all there was in the house to eat. I crept into her lap and I tried with my hands to take the pain from the bruises on her face and in her eyes.

"That's so you'll never forget me," I heard Jerry say, and the door closed behind him.

Chapter SIX

I got to my feet and went to the sink where there was a mirror. The damage wasn't too bad, thank God. One side of my face was swollen but at least it wasn't marked, and it didn't look as though I was going to have a shiner, which I was thankful for. I got the swelling down by using cold, wet towels so I could go on for the next show, but there wasn't a thing I could do about my bruised feelings.

I thought to myself, Now I know how my mother must have felt when Pop hit her. The physical pain isn't so bad, you get over that, and the humiliation of being hit by a man which is bad enough, but when it comes from a man you love, it's a real pain and it feels like you can't stand it and you'll never get over it. That wasn't the last time a man hit me, but I never took it so hard again because later on it didn't come from someone I loved. They say you can't remember pain, but every time I think of Jerry, to this day, I can feel a kind of echo of what I felt in that dressing room. And when I dream about him, which I do from time to time, I usually wake up with my teeth all clenched together and my mouth pressed into the pillow and my hands in fists. Sometimes I have to hit the pillow again and again before I can get back to sleep.

When we got back to New York, I promised myself that I was going to get Jerry out of my system one way or another. That slap in the face coming right on top of that wonderful week we had together was just too much. I think that a man who hits a woman is the lowest thing crawling around and I was not going to have any more of Mr. Jerry Miller in my life if I could help it. And yet I knew, and I know I said this before but I'll say it again, that in spite of everything, I was still in love with him, and if he called I would succumb again and go to bed with him, even though my pride as a woman told me that I really didn't like the way he treated me and that he was really no good for me, no matter how much I loved him.

We opened in the Latin Quarter and then almost at once we signed for a club date in Las Vegas for sometime about ten weeks off. We started to rehearse some new material for Vegas because I had an idea that we could imitate the styles of the other singing acts and build a whole routine about it: the Brandi Sisters' impressions of the competition. All of this took up a lot of time and kept me very busy, so I didn't have too much time to think about my personal problems. I went on dating but I tried to keep it down to a minimum, though I slept with some of the guys because I figured that the more affairs I could put between me and Jerry, the quicker I would kill this idea I had that I was still in love with him and always would be. My name still showed up in the columns and my sisters started sniping at me again, but I went right on until Angie came up with a new arranger who was going to work on our material.

Bob Ford was a bright young songwriter who had a lot of hit songs out already and a couple of hit shows, too. He was very good-looking and dashing in a debonair, man-about-town kind of way, and in fact he reminded me of Cary Grant. He had a warm, wonderful personality, and he and I dug each other right away. I used to love to sit and talk to him about music and songs and how we were able as a sister act to sing in such good harmony, even though none of us could read a note of music, because our father had taught us to sing by ear. We started going out together. Bob was a lot of fun to be with, and though I could tell that he was interested in me, he never tried to get me to go to bed with him, which I really appreciated. In fact, I started to think that maybe I had finally met a guy who looked at me as a human being and not just as a piece of bed meat.

This went on for about two months, until one night he dropped me home after a date and I walked into the apartment and there was Jerry sitting on the couch having a drink and Billie standing around looking very uncomfortable. Bob and I had had a great evening together and

53

I was still in a kind of glow. He had seen me up to the door of the apartment to say good night and good-bye, because the next day he was going to a place he had in Westhampton for a week to work on our arrangements. He said that any time he wanted peace and quiet, all he had to do was go out to Westhampton. He had kissed me good night very warmly but without getting too passionate and I had opened the door and come in, and there was Jerry to bring back all the bad memories and a few good ones I would rather have forgotten.

"What are you doing here?" I said, trying to fight down that old feeling of excitement at seeing him.

"I dropped by to have a little talk with you."

"The last time we had a little talk it ended with me on the floor."

"It's for your own good," he said.

"Oh, yeah? What are you selling this time, cancer?" Which is the punchline for a very bad joke that was going the rounds at the time, about a hooker in Miami.

"Maybe I better leave," Billie said.

"No, stick around, Billie," I told her. "Anything he's got to say to me, you can hear, too." I didn't want to be left alone with him. I was taking no chances.

"Maybe you'd better go, Billie," he said. "Because this concerns a third party." Billie looked at me and hesitated. "Don't worry, I won't hit her," he said.

Billie went into the bedroom and closed the door.

"I see in the columns that you and Bob Ford have been having quite a fling."

"That's not exactly any of your business."

"Excuse me, but I disagree. It is my business because I have a special interest in you."

That really got me mad. The prick had some nerve!

"You mean as a punching bag, right?"

"Now, wait a minute, Nina. I'm sorry about that, I really am. I just lost my temper."

"Or maybe you're interested in me because I'm another notch on your gun. A couple of more notches on that thing and you won't have anything left to screw with."

He took a deep breath and started over.

"I just want to tell you that you are in for a big surprise. This joker you're dating happens to be AC-DC."

I didn't know what the hell he was talking about.

"You lost me," I told him. "AC-DC. That's something about voltage in an apartment or a house, right? You mean he's a bad electrician?"

"I mean he swings both ways. He likes boys, too, as well as the girls."

"Oh, come on," I told him. "You can do better than that, can't you? I mean, I can understand your being jealous, but honestly, this is the limit."

"All right," he said, "I told you. Now you can find out for yourself, and when you do, I hope you'll have the decency to call me up and tell me that I was right."

I was suddenly very tired and anxious to get rid of him, because I felt that he was really trying to get me interested again by playing this big-brother act, and I figured that if he had to stoop to a trick like that he was really beneath me.

"OK, Jerry," I said. "You said your piece, and I get the message. Now would you mind leaving, because I've got a headache."

He picked up his hat and walked to the door and he turned to look at me, but when I said "Good night, Jerry," he knew I meant it and he left. It was months before I spoke to him again.

A week later, Bob came back from Westhampton with the arrangements all worked out, and he called me up and asked me to go to a party. I was very glad to hear from him because all that week I had not gone out with anyone else. In fact, for some weeks I had just been going out with Bob because I really thought we might have something very good going between the two of us, and I had hopes.

Anyhow, the night of the party, I met Bob at his apartment and we went to a very swank co-op building on Park Avenue somewhere in the Eighties. The apartment the party was in was a gorgeous duplex and the people at the party went with it. There were about ten or twelve couples, all beautiful people wearing expensive tans from Bermuda and the south of France and expensive clothes from Brooks Brothers and Balenciaga and jewels from Tiffany, the works. I had never met any of them before but I recognized some of the names, including the writer of a very famous syndicated gossip column called "Top Secret." "Top Secret" used to run stories about the hidden sex lives of celebrities. I always wondered how come the guy was never sued for libel and I guess everybody else did at the time, but he never was for some reason, and so the people who read "Top Secret" must have thought it was all the truth, right? Anyhow, this columnist and his wife were throwing the party, and when Bob introduced me to them, the wife said, "Oh my, Bob, but you've plucked yourself a nice little ripe one," which I didn't understand at the time. In fact I thought it was a funny thing to say about someone you've just met, but I let it pass.

We were all in this beautiful living room with ultra-modern furniture and paintings on the wall which I didn't dig, though I could see they must have cost a fortune because they were all signed and beautifully framed. I saw one with the name Picasso on it and I certainly knew who he was, so I was impressed. Drinks were served and there were delicious little things to eat, like tiny smoked oysters and a lot of shellfish things which everybody seemed to make a joke out of for some reason.

Then the hostess said, "Hurry and drink up, everybody, so we can get to our games."

I picked up my ears at that because I love party games.

"What are the games like?" I asked Bob. "I'm a great gin player and I just love Scrabble and things like that."

Everybody howled like mad, which surprised me because I didn't think I had said anything very funny.

Bob patted my hand and said, "Look, Nina, just remember you're with me. You're a woman and you've been around some, not a lot but a little, so you're going to learn a few things tonight. Don't forget, I want to be proud of you, so just join in the fun, all right?"

"I'm willing," I said, and then the games started, but I couldn't understand what was going on. First two men went out of the room together, and then two girls went out, and this went on for a while with people going out and coming back and some of them going out again with other people. Then somehow or other it was my turn and they sent me out of the room with the hostess. She was a beautiful, tall, willowy blonde who had once been an actress, though she hadn't been in the business for many years, and she was wearing a set of lounging pajamas that must have come straight from Paris and her hair was all upswept and done just beautifully. We went into the library and she shut the door and locked it and looked at me like I was supposed to do something.

"What do we do?" I asked her. "Are we supposed to have a secret or something?"

"Oh, come on," she said. "You may look naïve and innocent but I don't think you really are."

"I don't get it."

"You've been broken in, haven't you?"

I thought I understood by the tone of her voice.

56

"If you mean have I been laid, yes, I have, many times. So what? What's going on?"

She sighed as though she was getting impatient and said, "Come over here and sit down."

I sat down on a very comfortable sofa which was just about big enough for two and she took a book down from a shelf and sat next to me. The cover of the book said *The Wind in the Willows.* It had a very pretty picture of little animals running around, but, let me tell you, the only thing about wind in that book was from all the blowing that was going on. It was filled with the dirtiest, filthiest pictures I have ever seen, first with men and women together, completely naked, doing all kinds of things to each other, and then there were men together with men and women with women. And of course almost everything was either with the mouth, or up the ass, and it really disgusted me. I was certainly no shrinking violet at the time and I thought I knew a couple of tricks myself, but this was too much and none of it was anything I would buy. This gal I was with really dug it though, because she started breathing hard in my ear and moving closer and I felt her arm go around my waist. Then she closed the book and put it on an end table and put both arms around me and tried to kiss me.

"Hey, wait a minute!" I said, backing away. "What's going on?"

"Well, honey," she said. "That's the game. You and I make the scene together."

I said, "What?" because I really couldn't believe I had heard right. She opened the top of her pajamas and she took my hand and put it inside and I pulled it out right away.

"What's the matter, honey?" she whispered, putting her face close to mine. "Don't you swing both ways?"

I jumped up and backed away and she looked annoyed.

"Don't you rock?" she said.

"Would you mind opening the door?" I said. "I'm leaving."

"Oh, dear," she said, pouting like a little baby.

"Look, honey," I told her, "I've been in show business a long time and I've seen and known a few female impersonators, but I definitely do not dig them and I don't associate with them."

"But, darling," she said in a very quiet voice, "you're practically engaged to one."

That was too much for me.

"Please open the door," I said.

She unlocked the door and we went back to the living room.

"Bob," she said, "I think you've made a mistake. You'd better get rid of this one because she doesn't know where she's at."

"The hell I don't," I said. "Bob, would you please take me home?"

"But the party's just *starting!*" he said, and I noticed that the way he said it sounded almost like a woman.

"Please take me home, or do I have to get my own cab?"

By this time, everybody who was in the room was listening and watching and there were knowing smiles on some faces and looks being exchanged and so forth.

"Get your own cab, darling," he said, and turned away.

"That suits me fine," I told him. "And while we're at it, don't call me again!" and I left.

When I got home I sat down by myself and started to think. I figured that if I was starting to get involved with people like Bob Ford and his friends, then it must be because of my reputation—otherwise, why would a fag like Bob want to date me in the first place? If that was the way my life was going to go, I wanted no part of it, so I made up my mind right there and then: no more men until I had a chance to straighten myself out. I was going to keep myself out of the columns and out of other people's beds maybe for a year or so and then perhaps I could start with a clean slate. Then I started feeling very blue and depressed about Bob. It had seemed like such a good thing, and now I felt as though I would never be able to trust anyone again. How do you know who's what? That was the question I kept asking myself as I went to bed and finally to sleep.

By the time we got to Las Vegas, I felt a lot better about everything. I was very glad to get away from New York where I might run into Jerry, and I had definitely made up my mind to change my ways and start a new life. I wasn't going to push by looking and seeking for someone or something special. I was just going to relax and take it easy and try to get to live with myself, because I had the feeling that fate was about to be a little kind to me for a change.

We checked into the hotel, changed into shorts and bathing suits because it was about one hundred and ten degrees in the shade, and went down to the rehearsal hall.

Up on the bandstand was a very good-looking young man with a terrific tan and hair so blond it looked like fine spun gold. And along with this golden hair went dark eyebrows and black eyes. He looked like he was about twenty-five, but later on that week I discovered that in fact he was much older than me. He was running through his routine and we sat down and watched for a while.

Brace Fontaine had made a big noise out in Hollywood in a film called "Laugh, Clowns." It was a kind of biography of all the famous old-time vaudeville comedians put together, and now he was attracting a lot of attention on the club circuit. He was the big star attraction on our bill, and we were all given to understand before we left New York that he was a big success in Vegas and that anything he said was just great with the management. My sisters thought he was the most beautiful thing they had ever seen in pants, but there was something that I thought was very phony and conceited about him which I didn't like.

When he finished his routine, which I thought was only so-so, he came over and introduced himself and sat down and ordered coffee for everybody. The bellboy who was on special duty with the entertainers brought us our coffee, but Brace had his delivered to the table by a chorus girl. She was a real peach, the kind men just drip saliva over, with the big bust practically tearing her leotard apart and the well-rounded backside and narrow waist, a blonde of course, with her hair made up like Marilyn Monroe with the lock falling over one of her big blue eyes and a mouth too full and red to believe.

"Here, you're perspiring," she said, and draped a towel around his neck.

He looked up at her like he was a little annoyed and said, "Thank you. I'm busy now talking to the girls. I'll be there in a minute." Little Miss Tight-Ass gave us all a snide look and went back to her sister chorus girls. Then we got down to business, which was the real reason for his sitting down with us. He asked us what songs we were doing and I told him the numbers and that we did about forty-five minutes to an hour.

He shook his head and said, "That's too long. You'll have to cut it down to about thirty-five minutes."

My sisters looked at me and a kind of signal passed between us that said "Get going, Grandma," which I proceeded to do.

"Well now, look, Brace, our act is all planned."

"Sure, I understand. But I just want to make one thing clear. I'm the boss of the show and I bought you girls."

"All right, you're the boss, but before we get too dramatic about it, you should also know that we have an extra ten-minute number that we just learned. It's our biggest and it's really terrific."

"What's it like?"

"Impressions."

"Forget it. I do impressions. I do Cagney, Bogart, Stewart, Tracy, Colman, the whole Hollywood crowd. It's a great routine, and we can't have any more impressions on the bill."

"We don't do four Cagneys or Bogeys," I told him. "We do the singing acts. It's really sensational."

"Impressions of singing acts don't go," he said impatiently. "The Carter Sisters tried it in Chicago and it laid a big fat egg. It doesn't work."

"All right, then let's put it this way," I said, holding on to my temper, "if it doesn't go over when we open tomorrow night, we'll take it out of the act."

He started to shake his head again, so I said, "It's either that or give us our fare and we'll go back on the next train."

That really stopped him. I don't suppose he had ever tried to do business with a woman before and he probably never expected a woman to be as ballsy as me, because he just looked at me and didn't know what to say. My sisters were afraid to look at me, and I was afraid to breathe, because the truth of the matter was that this engagement meant a lot to us. We were all in hock in one way or another, especially me, since Billie and I owed about a thousand dollars back rent, and we were supposed to get five thousand a week for four weeks in Vegas, so I was really playing a long shot being so tough with this guy.

I looked him right in the eye and waited for his answer. I could see that his eyes were really beautiful, almost like a woman's. They were deep, velvety black which was stunning against his tan and blond hair, and his lashes were so long that when he closed his eyes they lay on his cheek, they really did. Any woman would have given a year of her life for those lashes, but that only made me like him even less. I also had the feeling that when he wanted to, he used those lashes and eyes to raise hell with any woman who was unlucky enough to be looking at him, but right then he wasn't doing any batting around with his eyes. Instead he was concentrating on me, and I could almost hear the wheels turning and the gears going into action.

"You're the Grandma of this act, aren't you?" he said. "I've heard about you. You're Nina, right?"

"That's right," I said. "And if we can't do the act we want to do, forget the engagement."

He drummed with his fingers on the table a little, thinking it over, and then he said with a smile, "OK, beautiful Grandma. Do the impressions. I hope for your sake they go over, because if they don't, remember, out of the act."

"It's a deal," I said, and he went back to his chorus girls.

Later on during our rehearsal I saw him come back into the hall and sit on a chair turned backwards, watching us. He didn't say anything after we were finished and we didn't run over to him and ask him what he thought. Instead, we went back to our room, showered and changed, had dinner, and then went to the casino. We all loved to play blackjack but we were always careful in Vegas, because if you don't watch yourself there you can lose all the big money the management pays you for performing. While we were sitting at the blackjack table, I looked over at the maître d's booth and there was Brace, smiling at me and motioning for me to come over to him.

"Excuse me," I told my sisters. "I better see what Little Boy Beautiful wants."

As soon as I got to him, he said, "I want to ask you to forget this afternoon. I was a little tired from rehearsing and my manners weren't too good."

"Neither was your professionalism," I told him, not giving him an inch, because I never do with the people I do business with, unless it pays. "I hope we're not having four weeks of that."

"Don't worry about it," he said. "It won't happen again. Listen, how would you like to run over to the Silver Nugget and catch Helen Traubel and Jimmy Durante?"

"I think I'd rather gamble for a while."

"Please, I want to apologize in style."

I thought to myself, What the hell, it wasn't good business to antagonize the boss, and maybe it was time to give an inch for the sake of good relations, so I went with him. As we walked out, I saw my sisters giving me the eye with guns and daggers, so I made the three-ring sign at them to let them know everything was under control.

Driving over to the Silver Nugget, he said, "You know,

Nina, I've caught your act a couple of times, once in New York and once in Miami, and I've always wanted to meet the cute one in the middle but I've never had the chance until now."

I thought to myself, If this guy tells me he fell in love with me watching me on the stage, I'm jumping out of the car at the next traffic light.

"Well, you've met me now. Was it worth waiting for?"

He looked at me and grinned.

"You digging for compliments? Because you don't have to, you know."

"I don't dig for anything," I told him.

"The answer is yes, definitely yes. In fact, maybe it's better my meeting you now than before, because now I can ask you out."

Something clicked in my mind and that little warning bell went *ting!*

"You're married, aren't you?"

"Well, in a way. I'm in the process of getting a divorce."

"I don't remember reading about your divorce, so I guess the way in which you're married is that you're still married, right?"

"I'm still married," he admitted, "but I am definitely getting divorced."

Here we go again, I said to myself. Maybe I'd better get out right now. As if he was reading my thoughts, he said, "I know that a lot of guys have probably tried to con you into thinking that they were free when they were really not, so let me give it to you straight. My wife, believe it or not, fell in love with my best friend, and we're getting a very nice friendly divorce."

"That's cozy," I said, waiting to hear more.

"Very cozy for her," he said. "Especially as she gets to keep our house and the kid and she'll be well taken care of all the way around. I make a lot of money and there's no problem there. And now let's talk about you."

That was his way of trying to direct the conversation, you understand. I went along because it really didn't make any difference one way or the other.

"I'll be honest with you," I told him. "I'm getting over a romance. I was very much in love with a guy and I think that maybe I still am, but it was just no good. He was no good for me."

"Would I be nosy if I asked who the guy was?"

"You can ask. Jerry Miller."

"Oh yeah, a second-rate comic."

"That's not very nice coming from you," I said, a little huffy, and surprised to find myself standing up for Jerry. "Not since I saw that blonde gofer you picked out of the line. Does she always carry your towel for you?"

"You don't miss a trick, do you?" he said, and he didn't sound so happy anymore.

"Don't be flattered," I told him. "It's not because I'm interested in you. Observing people, especially men, is a hobby of mine."

He didn't say anything for a while, but when we pulled up at the Silver Nugget he kept the jockey waiting for the car while he talked to me.

"Let's not start the evening off by being at each other's throats," he said. "Let's start over and get off on the right foot, because I really do like you."

"Now listen, Brace," I told him, trying to sound very businesslike and unemotional, "I've been through a lot for my young years and I don't want to get involved with anybody. I'm just here to work Las Vegas again. The money's good and I intend to cool everything else for a while."

"Was he that wonderful?"

"As a matter of fact, he was the first man since my father to lay a hand on me."

He took that very big and made quite a fuss over it.

"If I ever meet up with him," he said, "I'm going to knock him flat on his ass for doing that to you."

"Forget it," I said. "It's over and done with. He may not be easy to forget but I'm trying. I really want to get the guy out of my system, so do you mind if we don't spend the evening talking about Jerry Miller?"

He bought that, and we caught Traubel and Durante and then had supper together. He told me his whole life story, which was pretty grim. In fact, if anything, it was a lot worse than mine because he never had any family like I did. His folks were divorced when he was only a baby. Then his father remarried and moved away and his mother ran off with a salesman and left him with an aunt who didn't care for his mother or him. His childhood was a nightmare with his aunt beating him one minute and loving him up the next and finally when he was fifteen he ran away and bummed around for a while. At last he got to Hollywood where he started working as an extra, which is how he got his big break. The producer, Sam Garrick, saw him on the lot one day, liked his looks, gave him a screen test and put him in a supporting role in one of his pictures. That's the same Sam Garrick of Sam and Joye Garrick, only I didn't know them yet. According to Brace, it was only uphill after that with the Garricks helping him every step of the way, and in particular, Joye Garrick.

I must have looked at him as though I was saying, So you got to be a star on the casting couch, so what else is new, because he said, "It wasn't the way you think. The Garricks are very happily married. In fact they're quite a team. They're both going to be here for the opening and you'll meet them and see for yourself. She took me under her wing and helped me along the way. What's so terrible about that?"

We sat around and talked some more and somewhere along the way I let slip how important this engagement was to us financially, and that made him admire me even more because now he realized how much I had gambled when I stood up to him. He took me back to the hotel and said good night without making any kind of a pass.

The next day was just like any other opening. We were busy all day getting our gowns pressed and doing the last-minute things to our makeup, and we all had the usual opening-night jitters and butterflies. We were in our dressing rooms at six-thirty, which shows how nervous we were because the first show didn't go on until eight. It was the new routine in the act, the impressions, that made us so nervous, and when there was a knock on the door we all jumped out of our skins. It was a bellboy with four dozen roses and a beautiful card that said, "Knock 'em dead tonight, impressions and all, love, Brace," which we all thought was very sweet and it made the girls feel a lot better about him.

The opening act went on and then the dancer and then it was our turn. We made that audience flip its lid. They loved us all the way through, and when we went into the impressions routine the roof came down, or went up, whatever you want to say. I was trying very hard because I really wanted to show Brace how good we could be and I guess we all felt the same way because I could sense that every one of us was putting a little something extra into all the numbers that night. He came back during the intermission to congratulate us and tell us that we were the greatest group he had ever seen and then the intermission was over and he was on. Angie and I went out into the audience to catch his act and we did not care for it. We both thought it was pretty corny and that the only thing that was putting him over was his looks and a kind of cute way he had with the audience. The great impressions routine came at the end and you could see that it was his reputation from the picture that was carrying him through because he really wasn't that good. Later on, he came out in a lavender sweater and white pants, which knocked all the cigarette girls off their feet, and invited us out with him. He asked us how we liked his part of the show. Angie said that he was great, which saved the day, because it's always hard for me to say something I don't believe, and the most enthusiastic I could get was to tell him that he was very good.

He had a table reserved at the Casino, and after a while Joye Garrick and her husband showed up. She and Brace kissed very warmly but I could see from the way they kissed and the way Sam looked at them that Brace had been telling the truth, that there wasn't any sex between them. Joye looked like what she was, a well-preserved former actress who was growing old gracefully, as the saying goes. Later on when I got to know her better she told me that she was in her early forties. I could see that she spent a lot of time over her face because that was still very young-looking, but her arms were starting to show that loose fat just above the inside of the elbow that goes with the fifties. Sam was Sam, just like he is today, a nice friendly guy who called everybody "Ace" and had a glad handshake for everyone he met, but I had the feeling that behind the glad hand was a mind like a steel trap.

After opening night, Joye and Sam and Brace and I made a regular foursome. He would have tables reserved at all the different clubs, and after the last show we would go out on the town and have a ball. It helped me forget Jerry, and it gave me the feeling that for the first time in a long time things were going my way. We had a successful act going, we were raking in good money, and I had the best-looking guy in town dating me, even though I still couldn't like him as much as he liked me. I also had a chance to see how much the Garricks thought of Brace, and if I still had any idea that there had ever been anything between Joye and Brace, it disappeared watching the way those two fussed over him. She didn't mind at all when he paid me a good deal of attention and he was always doing that. She just smiled at him like a loving mother watching a son with his first girlfriend, and I had the feeling that maybe that's what they were to each other. Sam and Joye were the mother and father Brace had never known and he was the child they had never had. They were also very anxious to see Brace get ahead in his career, and they kept telling him about how they were inviting all kinds of people to Las Vegas to catch the show, producers and directors and the heads of movie studios.

The last week of the show Brace asked me one night if we were going back to New York after the show closed and when I said we were, Sam said, "That's where you ought to go, Brace. There's a lot of big action going on in New York."

"That's right, honey," Joye said. "And we know the guy to see there, too. We'll get you together with him and I guarantee that inside of a year you'll be running the town."

Brace looked at me and said, "That's a thought. How would you feel about that, Nina? If I came to New York, I mean?"

I just kind of shrugged and looked as though it didn't mean a thing in the world to me, which it really didn't. All I could say was, "It's up to you."

Later on that night when he took me back to the hotel he said, "I suppose you'll be moving back in with your roommate."

"No, I don't think so," I told him. "Billie is going to Toledo. . . . I'll move in with Mom. . . ."

"You know who else is moving into your mother's house in Brooklyn?" he said.

I looked at him, and from the way he was staring at me I knew what he was going to say before he actually said it.

"Me!" he said.

"You?" I looked at him as though he was out of his mind.

"Do you think I'm going to let you go after this?" he said. "I've just got to get to know you. I want to eat your mother's spaghetti. I want to get to know your whole family. Because, you know something, you're the girl I'm going to marry."

For four weeks we had been going out and I must say that during all that time he had never once stepped out of line. About the most that had happened was a couple of good-night kisses and not too many of those, and the rest of the time he had been a perfect gentleman and a wonderful date. In fact, I had changed my opinion about him quite a bit and I felt that given time I might get to

66

like him, though I didn't think I could ever love him. Jerry still had the market cornered, after all, but I knew I could never go back to Jerry and that my only hope was if some really nice guy came along whom I could at least like and who thought of me as something else besides a bed warmer.

"Don't you think you should get rid of your first wife before you marry me?" I said. I just couldn't resist that one, no matter how nice he was acting.

"That was below the belt, honey."

"I didn't mean it that way," I told him. "What I mean is that you shouldn't talk marriage to me because I don't want to get involved with anyone, let alone marry him. Not right now."

I let him take me into his arms, not too closely, and he said, "Nina, I'll never try to force you into anything," and he kissed me.

God, I wish I had had you there that night, all hooked up and ready to record!

Chapter
SEVEN

A week later we were back in New York, and I was asleep one morning in my mother's house in Brooklyn when I heard the doorbell ring in her apartment upstairs and she came down and said, "Nina, it's that Brace Fontaine. He's here!"

Would you believe it, he was! He flew in that morning from the coast and came straight from the airport, ready to move in and live with my family. Of course I had told Mom all about him when we got back from Vegas, because even though I really didn't expect him to follow through, I thought there was at least an outside chance he might and I didn't want her to be surprised.

"Honey," she said when I told her, "as long as he doesn't treat you like a good-time girl. You know, with these married men you have to be careful. After all, look what happened with Jerry Miller, and he seemed so nice at the beginning, remember? But if this Brace will make you happy, then it's OK with me. As long as you're not breaking up his marriage."

"That was broken before I met him," I told her. "And I didn't say he would make me happy. I don't really know him. Besides, there's something about him I don't understand. Don't ask me what, because I can't put my finger on it yet. Maybe I'm all wrong because after all he was always a gentleman with me and he wasn't ever fresh like all the other guys, or phony like Jerry. But still, I don't know. If I get tired of him or if he gets out of line, he can always get a hotel room in Manhattan, right?"

And now there was my mother wearing her best manners and using that special voice she uses on the telephone and with strangers, saying, "Of course I know who you are. How about some breakfast?" and then running downstairs to see if I was getting dressed and then running back upstairs into her other voice. By the time I got up there, Brace was sitting in the kitchen, ready to dig into a plate of bacon and eggs.

"I told you I'd move in," he said to me.

He moved in all right, he moved in on Mom and my sisters and he moved in on me, too, in more ways than one. Inside of a week he had the family eating out of his hand, including me, I won't deny that. He took us everywhere, to all the fun places and nightclubs and restaurants, the whole family, even Angie and Marcie and their husbands. They were in on it too. Every other night was New Year's Eve for the Brandis. If it wasn't another theater, it was another fancy restaurant, or out to Belmont for the races or maybe a day at Palisades Amusement Park just for laughs. It was like he had adopted us, like he was trying to make up for not having a family himself. I guess in his own way he was really getting a big kick out of it, with the home-cooked lasagne and the spaghetti sauces he was so crazy about and the homey atmosphere all around him, because my mother and sisters being the wonderful family they were made him feel like he was part of it all and really at home.

Naturally he paid a lot of special attention to yours truly because, after all, whose benefit was it all for, right? At the beginning it was mostly gifts.

The first couple of times I got suspicious and told him to stop, but he said, "Look, I'm not trying to buy you. It's just that I can't pass a store without thinking of you and getting you something. Please let me do it because it makes me happy." So I let him buy me the charm bracelets in Cartier's and the mink stoles at Bendel's and the perfumes from Balenciaga and all the other little expensive things. I figured to myself, What the hell! If he wants to, why not! After all I wasn't putting out, was I? And I wasn't making any promises, either. That's how I thought at that age.

This went on for a couple of weeks and then he got called back to the coast to do a feature film. He was gone for about six weeks and every day there was another letter or postcard from him. What a switch that was for me, being on the receiving end of the daily mail, with the "I love you's" and the crosses and circles for kisses and hugs coming my way and not the other way around like it used to be with Jerry. And once United Parcel brought a package and when I opened it, it was an emerald bracelet watch.

"Oh, Nina!" Mom said, putting her hands together like she was praying.

"Mom, you can't put a price tag on a relationship."

"But he's so wonderful! He hasn't been fresh with you and he's been so wonderful to us."

"But Mom, you know that every guy ultimately has sex in the back of his mind."

"Not Brace. I think he genuinely loves you and he's going to wait until you get married."

I said to myself, Whoa! What am I getting myself into here! So I figured maybe I'd better put the record straight once and for all.

"Look, Mom," I told her, "I would love to fall in love and get married and sing for maybe just a few more years and then have a couple of kids and really settle down, you know. But I just don't know if this is it!"

"Nina, it's got to be. Why else would he——!"

"It may be that way with him. I just don't know if it's that way with me."

"Oh, Nina. It just has to be. You don't know what it's like to have only one man in your life. That's how it was with me, honey, and there's never been anybody since."

I looked at her when she said that and said, "God bless you for it, Mom." She was still a good-looking woman. After all, she was only in her late forties then, and there was still a lot of that dark Sicilian beauty left. She wore her hair back, and with her forehead so high and wide, and her lovely dark eyes and the delicate cheekbones so fine under the skin, and the perfect nose and chin and her mouth curved just right when she smiled but not too full, she looked like Dolores del Rio. You couldn't tell that she had three false teeth in front which we had made her go to the dentist for as soon as we started making good money. And if she was a little heavy in the bust and hips, so what! After four kids, what did you expect, right? She had been a widow for almost ten years and she never once in all that time looked at another man or went out with anyone.

I thought to myself about all the years of poverty she had been through, all those years sitting home alone night after night while her husband was out with her kids playing cheap dates for a couple of measly bucks. And I thought about the other nights when he was out on his own meeting other women. She knew about that. He could never hide the truth from her. It was in his eyes and the way his hands would twitch and how he lost his temper if she asked too many questions. Why he even made it with her best friend one night after Momma got tired and went to bed and left them sitting together on the living room sofa. She told me so herself because the friend had a bad conscience and told her. And here she was, talking like marriages are made in heaven and hers was a Garden of Eden. She was forgetting what it was really like. All she did after Pop died was go to church to play bingo, sometimes five nights a week. That's how she lived the rest of her life. Why, Momma? The church was with you. You were a widow. Why? Were you afraid of taking a chance on another man? Was he that wonderful when you first married, before all the frustration and sickness killed him inside? Were you still in love with the young Rosanno? You never told me, Momma, and I never asked. I wish I had. Instead I said, "God bless you, Mom," and put on the watch.

Brace finished his scenes in the picture and came flying back into the arms of the Brandis. We all went out to Idlewild to meet him and there was a big reunion right in the terminal. It was like a brother or a husband coming home—that was the way he acted and that was how my family acted toward him. I wasn't sure how I felt. I liked him more in Brooklyn than I did in Las Vegas, but I wasn't in love with him. I liked the gifts and all the attention he was paying me because I'm the kind of a woman who needs a lot of attention, and it appealed to my vanity having this gorgeous guy with all the money in the world falling all over me.

During that time, while he was living with us and while he was making the picture, I hadn't gone out with anybody else, but when he tried to get me to go out to the coast with him—I didn't tell Mom about that—I said no. He said he didn't know how he was going to get along without me for six weeks, but we had a couple of club dates to play in New York so I had a good excuse. When he went I can't say I was sorry to see him go, but I can't say that I was pleased either. And when he came back I was glad to see him but I didn't fall all over him either. All the time I kept saying to myself, What am I getting into? This is really getting serious. It was as though something was moving through my life that I couldn't stop. It was just carrying me along and somehow I didn't have the willpower to jump off. I think what was really in the back of my mind was that old crazy hope that maybe this was finally it. It was the way I had felt about Bob and now I felt the same thing about Brace, except I had really dug Bob, and I really didn't dig Brace. And yet I felt that I didn't want to pass up a chance to settle down and be happy, whatever that means. Like Jerry said, always the romanticist, right?

When we got back from the airport with Brace, he opened his flight bag and started taking out presents. There was something for everyone. Beautiful pottery for Mom that he found in an expensive place on Wilshire Boulevard, little Italian peasants with donkey carts all covered with flowers and peasant girls dancing and men with moustaches playing the accordion. It wasn't cheap stuff, let me tell you, and there was French perfume for my sisters at twenty-five bucks a half ounce; he bought the stuff like it was toilet water.

He had a big cardboard box that he had brought off the plane with him, and he said, "Mom, this is for your baby," and put it down in front of me.

I opened it and inside was a fur coat, a Russian sable. My sisters squealed, and my mother clapped her hands together and said, "Oh, my God! Put it on, Nina! Quick! Put it on."

I didn't know what to say. Brace was looking at me and so were my sisters, and my mother looked so happy you'd think it was her coat. I put it on, and there was a hood and a muff, too. I can't really tell you how it felt to have that chocolate-brown soft warmness around me. It was richness like I had never seen or felt and at the same time it made me feel like I was a little girl again, but that's another story.

Dolores was the first one to get her breath.

71

"That can't be real," she said, and her voice was just dripping green.

"Is it real?" Mom asked Brace. She didn't believe it, either.

"It sure is, Mom!" Brace sounded like Russian sables grew on trees where he came from. "It's real, all right. All twenty thousand dollars' worth."

"You stole it!" she said.

Everybody laughed, and he said, "Nope, I didn't steal it. It's really hers. I paid for it."

I didn't know what to say. I kept thinking that I couldn't accept it and I should give it back, but what I said was, "I'll be scared to death to wear it." My voice didn't sound real to me, but I couldn't get myself to tell him I couldn't take it, not in front of everybody.

"It's fully insured," he told me, "so don't worry about wearing it."

"Twenty thousand!" Mom still couldn't get over it. Angie and Marcie ran their hands over it.

Brace put his arm around me and said, "Nina's my girl and I want everybody to know it."

Marcie said, "I don't think anybody will miss it when she wears that coat."

Marcie is the quiet, thoughtful one. She's the sister who's nearest in age to me, and though we're not as close as Angie and me, there is something special between us because we were the two youngest. We spent a lot of time playing together when the other two would shut us out. Sometimes Marcie is almost like my conscience, because I think she knows what I'm really like better than anyone else in the family. She ran her hand up and down the sleeve of the coat and she looked at me and smiled a little, but I couldn't smile back. I held the collar tighter around my neck and I felt Brace's hand on my shoulder and his arm around me and I said to myself, Why not! Right there and then I made up my mind that I would marry him when he got his divorce, and I would try hard to make the marriage work even if I didn't love him. At least, I would be able to thumb my nose at Jerry and say, See, you said it would never happen!

All that night I kept waking up and putting on the light to look at the coat hanging in my closet. The next day I put it on, and from then on I wore it every chance I could. By that time Billie had come back from Toledo, and the first time I met her for lunch and she saw the coat, she almost fell out of her seat.

72

"Oh, my gosh!" she said. "He must really love you to spend that kind of money. How do you feel about him?"

"I like him more than I did two months ago, but I don't think I'm in love."

Billie looked at me like she couldn't believe I was for real.

"Forget the love bit, Nina. And stop torching for Jerry, you jerk! You still haven't learned your lesson, have you?"

I tried to change the conversation but all she wanted to talk about was the coat and Brace, so I went along with her which was a big, fat cop-out because all I was doing was letting myself drift into a relationship I only wanted in a half-assed sort of way.

Brace went on living at my mother's house and everything went on like before, except now you could say that there was an understanding between us. He and I would sit around at night and have long, serious talks and he would put his arm around me even when the other members of the family were present, and when we were alone, he kissed me more than he had before. The kisses got longer and more passionate and we started to pet. We petted a little more each time, and each time we went a little further. I still wasn't in love with him, but he was attractive and it had been so long since I had done anything like this with a man, I started to enjoy it. And of course there was the extra spice of being guilty about doing it with my mother upstairs, or sometimes when we were parked in a car just outside the house.

The first place his hands went to was always my legs. He never really tried to get at my breasts, which really took me by surprise because that's where most guys start the campaign. Maybe once or twice he put a hand inside my blouse and felt them a little, but he never tried to get my brassiere unhooked and he never tried to kiss them. Usually, in the middle of a kiss I would feel his hand slip under my skirt and slide down my thigh. I never let him go too far, usually just a touch on the outside, maybe, and once or twice I let him slip a hand inside my panties and feel around. He got very excited at that and breathed hard and buried his face in my neck, but I felt myself getting carried away too, so I closed my legs and made him take his hand out. I never did go too much for heavy petting because I think it's cheap. If you're going to go that far you ought to go the whole way or not at all, right?

One night the whole scene blew up in my face. I was lying down with a headache. The rest of the family were

73

all at the church playing bingo and Brace was upstairs watching television on the big sixteen-inch set he had bought for Mom as a kind of rent payment. At that time, sixteen inches was the biggest but the twenty-inch sets were just around the corner and Brace was already talking about trading the sixteen for a twenty. Anyhow, after a while he came downstairs to see how I was feeling. The headache was still sort of coming and going behind my eyes, so he brought me a couple of aspirins. I had the lights off in the bedroom because they had hurt my eyes and Brace had to find his way over to the bed in the dark.

"Darling, are you all right?" he wanted to know. I told him I was feeling better.

"I worry about you when you're not feeling well," he said, sitting down on the edge of the bed.

I could make him out against the light from the street lamp coming in through the venetian blind. He leaned over me and kissed me and I kissed him back because I was touched by the attention he was paying me. I thought he was really being sweet, so I didn't object when he put his arms around me and kissed me again. Then he started kissing my ears and my eyes, and my mouth and neck. The house was very quiet. There wasn't the usual noise of people moving around upstairs or in the bathroom or kitchen, and I guess the feeling that we were completely alone, which didn't happen too often, got to both of us. I hadn't been to bed with a man in about five or six months by then and I guess I was overdue, because I could feel myself beginning to respond, but really respond.

Brace slid a hand down to my pajama bottoms and opened the snaps on the side. His hand slid around to my stomach and moved slowly down, pulling the pajamas down as it went. He slipped his fingers in between my legs right at the crotch, and it felt so good I opened my legs for him. He knew just where to put his fingers, and in a few seconds I was breathing through my mouth and moving his hand around with mine to show him where the best places were. The next thing I knew, he was pulling my pajama pants all the way down and then he was taking his own pants off and getting on top of me and in between my legs. I wanted him right that minute very badly, not him in particular, maybe, but someone, anyone, to push a hard thing into me because I was all hot and wet and dying for it. I pulled up my knees and spread my legs wider to make it easier for him, and when he fumbled around I put my hand down and helped him to find the

74

right place. He slid in with a deep sigh and then he groaned, because as soon as he was all the way in, he came. I felt him jerk and bump around inside and he groaned out loud again. I started to grind away at him, hot as hell now because I wanted to come myself before he lost his hard-on. Then all of a sudden I knew that someone else was in the room. I froze and tried to see who it was and then the lights came on and over Brace's shoulder I saw my mother's face.

At first I thought to myself, Caught! Isn't this a panic! By my own mother! Then I felt hot and cold all at once and my heart went down into my stomach and I felt sick, and wished I was anywhere else but in that bed. It was shame and guilt and disgust all at once, the way I felt that first time with Jerry all over again, only worse.

Mom had the kind of look on her face that you see on people who walk into the wrong room and are embarrassed, like a woman walking into a men's room by mistake. Then her expression changed and she said, "I want you both out of here in half an hour."

"Now, Mom, listen," I started to say, but it was like I wasn't talking.

"I don't want to listen to anything," she said, and she was looking right at Brace. "Just get out of here and take my daughter with you because she's not my daughter anymore."

"Now, wait just a minute, Mom," I said, but she was out of the room already. Brace got off me and went into the bathroom. I got up out of the bed and went into the kitchen. She was standing in the middle of the room with one hand up to her mouth like she was trying to figure something out.

"Now, Mom, look, it just happened. It was heading for that, anyhow."

"I never thought you would do anything like that in this house, not with me around," she said. Her voice was very quiet and low, like she was trying to hold on to herself. "There are motels for that."

"But, Mom, it's cheap to do something like that in a motel, isn't it? Look, I'm a grown girl now. I'm not a baby anymore. This is not the first time I've had sex with a man. Why are you so upset?"

She started to cry. The tears trickled down her face and all of a sudden her voice was hoarse and strained.

"I'm upset because he's married and now I see that's all

he wants from you. When is a man going to want you just for you?"

"I guess never," I said. "There isn't any such thing, I guess. That's the way the world is. You can't have a relationship with a man without having sex. He waited quite a few months for it and it just happened, Mom. I gave in, too, you know. I didn't exactly push him away."

"I know. That's what hurts me the most. Just leave, Nina. Leave and go with him and live with him, marry him, do what you want. I don't know anymore. I really have to have time to think. I'm so shocked that I could never have him living here again, and I don't want you running back and forth to his hotel, so live with him. Maybe it's better that way. But I don't want you here."

"Now look, Mom," I said, trying to make a little joke out of the situation. "You're not chasing me out of my own apartment, are you? After all, I pay for this house, too. This is my home, also."

"You can't stay here!" she cried at me. "I got a reputation, you know. The neighbors all know he's here and now he's never going to marry you and I don't know what I'm going to tell all of them, all my friends."

She started to cry hysterically.

"Mom, is that what you want? You want me to marry him? But I'm not really sure I love him."

She turned on me, looking wild and mad.

"You don't know if you love him? And you were doing that with him!"

"Mom, please don't be so old-fashioned. And don't push me into marriage, please."

"I'm not pushing you into anything!" she yelled at me. "And I won't speak to you until you are married! I can't take this anymore! Everybody has been putting you on a string and I won't stand for it! It's happening to my baby daughter and I can't stand to see it! So please leave now!"

I could see there wasn't anything more I could say that would make a difference, so I went back into the bedroom and started to pack an overnight bag. I felt like I was in the middle of a nightmare, with my mother in the kitchen crying her heart out and me packing to go somewhere, where I didn't know, because I didn't have a home anymore. I wished I would wake up and end it but I knew it was really happening and I couldn't wake up. Then the nightmare got worse. I saw Brace come busting out of the bathroom and go past me into the kitchen.

I heard him say, "Now listen to me, Mom, you're a

76

wonderful old-fashioned Italian mother and all that jazz, but you have to learn to mind your own goddamn business."

"That's the way you talk to me now!" she said. "You were so sweet to me before and I was such a wonderful mother and my cooking and my family is so wonderful and now because you laid with my daughter in bed you think you can curse at me!"

I got back into the kitchen as Brace was telling her, "You mind your own business, goddamn it. This is our lives, not yours."

"Brace, shut up!" I yelled at him. "You're talking back to my mother. Just take it easy, will you? You're making it worse!"

Dolores and Marcie came into the room, looking like they didn't understand what was going on, and the minute my mother saw them she suddenly got very dramatic. She pulled at her hair and she threw out her arms to them and screamed, "You should see the way he's talking to me! Just listen! He's cursing me. And he's been in bed with your kid sister and now he's cursing and swearing at me!"

"Goddamn it, now you stop saying that, you old—"

"Brace, cut it out. This is only going to lead to trouble. Let's just get out of here quietly."

I had him by the shirt front and I was shaking him and talking at him between my teeth, but he wouldn't listen and he wouldn't shut up.

"Kicking your own daughter out!" he shouted at her. "Who the hell do you think you are!"

"What's going on?" Marcie said, her voice shaking, and Dolores said, "For God's sake, shut up! You want the neighbors to hear you? Calm down, both of you!"

My mother drew herself up very straight and she walked over to Brace and looked him right in the eye and said, "I'll show you who I am. And I'll show you who you are, too!" Then she walked over to the kitchen phone, which happened to be a wall phone, and picked up the receiver.

"What are you doing with that phone?" Brace said to her.

"I'm calling the Los Angeles police," she said very calmly.

"Mom, what are you doing?" I said.

"Hello, operator," she said into the phone. "I want to make a call to Los Angeles, California, please." Then she said to us, "I'm going to report a married man committing

77

adultery with my daughter. I want those divorce lawyers out there to hear about this. And I want him arrested."

I didn't know whether to laugh or what. Then I saw Brace's face and I could see that he didn't think it was funny. He rushed at Mom, pushed her aside, grabbed the phone right off the wall and smashed it down on the floor as hard as he could. Then he ran over to the china closet and picked up all that porcelain he had bought Mom and threw it around the room, not really aiming at anybody but just throwing it so that it smashed all over the place. It was a wonder no one was hurt.

"Brace, for God's sake, stop!" I yelled at him. "What are you doing? This is my family! Stop!"

"They can't have any of my presents," he shouted at me. "Everything is over with them! Finished!"

Then he grabbed me by the arm and said, "Come on! Let's get out of here!"

I pulled away.

"Now, wait a minute, Brace!"

"You'd better go," my mother said, "because you can't stay here."

I ran back into the bedroom, picked up my bag, and started out with Brace. There was a swinging door between the kitchen and the dining room, and as he went out after me he grabbed it and shoved it hard behind him, like he was trying to slam it. I heard Marcie yell and scream, and when I looked back the door was open again and Mom was holding Marcie's head in her arms.

"He killed her!" she screamed at me. "He killed her! Help! Police!"

"Her nose is broken!" Dolores yelled. "The sonofabitch broke your sister's nose!"

Marcie lifted her head and her face was covered with blood.

The rest was just as unbelievable. We ran out into the street, Brace and I, with my mother running after us yelling for the police. Doors came flying open, windows had heads sticking out, and people were saying, "What's the matter? What's happening?" There was a bus up at the corner at a bus stop and we ran for it with the screaming in our ears. We made it just as it was about to pull away and we jumped on and sat down, out of breath. I thought to myself that it was like a B-movie and I didn't know what was happening to me. Then I looked out the back window of the bus and I saw my mother and some of the neighbors standing on the corner waving their arms, and some of the men ran after the bus, but they never caught up with it. I sat in the bus until we got to the Brighton Beach Line station at Avenue J, wondering what was going to happen to me.

Chapter
EIGHT

We took the subway to Manhattan, and all the way in I kept looking at this man sitting next to me as though he was a stranger. I must have been in a state of shock because I couldn't believe everything that had happened, and most of all I couldn't understand the way Brace had turned so violent all of a sudden. I kept thinking to myself, My God, what kind of a Jekyll and Hyde is he?

We found a hotel in the East Fifties, and Brace rented two apartments a few doors apart on the same floor because, without saying it to each other, we both knew we didn't want to spend that night together. I was very upset and stunned over the way Brace had put me into this fix with my family, though I figured I was just as much to blame as he was for letting myself go all the way with him. By this time I could see that he wasn't feeling too good about the situation. He looked tired and beat while we were at the desk registering, and when he said good night he promised me he'd try to make it up with my mother. He said he was sorry he had hurt Marcie and he would foot the doctor bills, and he sounded really ashamed and disgusted with himself. Even though I was angry with him, I also felt sorry for him and I kissed him good night, but once I got inside my apartment and closed the door behind me, the thought struck me that I was stuck with him. The very thing that I didn't want to happen had happened. I knew that I did not want to get so involved with Brace. Yet there I was really tied to the guy and on the outs with my family, because I didn't have any doubts about how my sisters would take all this. The whole thing was one big mess.

I took a couple of sleeping pills to get me through the night and I could have used a couple more the next day, because that was a continuation of more of the same only I had to live with it. In the morning Brace called my

79

mother on the phone and tried to apologize to her but she hung up on him right away. In the afternoon I had to go to a rehearsal with my sisters, and as soon as I walked into the rehearsal hall, the freeze hit me in the face like a wall of ice. Marcie's nose was swollen but she didn't have a shiner so I knew it wasn't broken, thank God, but it might just as well have been from the way my sisters looked at me. Nobody talked to me, which was very pleasant, let me tell you, if you can imagine four people singing together and rehearsing an act all afternoon with three of them not communicating with the fourth. When the session was over, Angie broke down a little and stayed behind after the others left.

"What the hell happened last night, Nina? Why did that nut hit Marcie?"

"He didn't mean to," I explained. "It was an accident. The whole thing was an accident."

"You mean him smashing all that stuff was an accident? And making it in bed with you? That was an accident, too, I suppose."

"Angie, it just happened. Believe me, I really didn't want that. I don't know what to do."

"I'll tell you one thing you better do and that's stay away from the house, because Mom doesn't want you around anymore. At least stay away until she calms down. And get rid of that lunatic before he ruins your life."

How's that for human nature? I thought to myself. A couple of days before, Brace was everybody's fair-haired boy, right? See what a little broken pottery can do? Still, that was the best piece of advice anybody ever gave me, I must admit, but I wasn't in the advice-taking mood that day because that night I slept in Brace's apartment. And the night after and the night after that, too, and so on and so forth until we decided it was silly to pay for two apartments when we were actually using only one. It wasn't that I dug Brace so much that I just had to sleep with him, but the way he seemed to be in love with me played up to my vanity. Besides, I was so damn hurt and blue and lonely, I felt so cut off from everything and everybody in my whole life, my mother, my sisters, just everything, that I needed someone to hang on to and Brace was it. I hung on and I went for the full ride all around the merry-go-round, only there weren't any brass rings.

I must admit that sex with Brace was pretty exciting in those days, though I thought it was a little weird. The second night we made it in bed, he went down on me. I had heard about that practice from some of my friends, and one or two of them said they liked it because it was a real thrill and different, but I felt kind of squeamish about a man putting his mouth there after he had kissed me and maybe would kiss me again. The first time I felt his head going down between my legs I said, "Hey, hey! Now, wait a minute," and tried to push him away.

"Why, what's the matter, baby?"

I didn't know how to say it, so I just looked at him and he understood right away.

"But it's nothing to be ashamed of, baby. It's perfectly natural, believe me. It's just like kissing your mouth. It's because I love you so much, I've just got to kiss you all over, even there. Just let me try it—all right?—and if you don't like it, I'll stop, I promise."

I said all right and I lay back waiting to see how it would be and it was pretty good. In fact the way he did it that first time, it was damn good. He was very gentle, kissing me all over my crotch and nuzzling into the hair so it tickled and made me giggle. Then he used two fingers to hold it open and he put his tongue in and sort of ran it all the way up. I could feel the sensation all the way up my back and I shivered and closed my eyes. Then he took that little bit in his mouth and spread my legs wider and his tongue went back down and as far in as it could go and his whole mouth was pressed against me there and he took in as much as he could between his lips and sucked hard. That was good but not as good as before, so I put my hands down on the back of his head and pushed it back up so he could grab the little bit again, and he sucked so hard I couldn't hold back and everything came pouring down and I came with the whole bed shaking under me.

I lay there panting and exhausted because it had been very intense, except that the inside of my vagina ached. I raised my head to look down at Brace and he was lying there with his head still between my thighs and his feet sticking out over the end of the bed. I could feel his breath on me, warm and sort of moist, coming very fast, and then he put his hands on my thighs and pushed them back so my legs were all the way up and he started sucking again. I went through the whole thing all over again, only this time I came sooner and not so strong but it was still good. He wanted to do it again and he would have gone right on only I made him stop because I was starting to feel a little tender down there and the ache was worse, and I knew that to really satisfy me I needed him inside. I asked him to do it that way but he said he had to go to the bathroom. He got off the bed and when I looked down I could see that the sheet where he had been laying was all messy because he had come all over it two or three times at least while he was working on me. When he came back, he rested a few minutes and then he got on me and we did it the usual way, only he came too soon and I had to hold him in and work fast to come the way I wanted.

I thought all this was weird and maybe just a little perverted, but I didn't mind too much. I figured that Brace was oversexed. He wasn't the first guy I had been to bed with who suffered from that complaint and, frankly, in those days I didn't object. I like a guy who's wild in bed and can shoot three or four holes a night. From then on that was our routine. He would go down on me a couple of times and then we'd wind up with a regular lay. The only trouble was that once he got inside he didn't seem to have much control but always came in a hurry. I had to watch out for that.

We went on this way for a couple of weeks, with me getting more and more used to being with him. It was like being married but without the real feeling of being married, if you know what I mean. He would leave in the morning at about eleven or twelve to see his agent or to talk to producers about some television show or feature film. I would walk my dog, my little cocker spaniel, Jackie, that I had had for about five years then. Then I would maybe go to a rehearsal in the afternoon with my still non-talking sisters or do some shopping on Fifth Avenue. We would both get back to the apartment by evening and I would either cook dinner or we would go out to a restaurant. Then I would go to the club, wherever it was, and sing with my sisters, and maybe he had an evening appointment somewhere, and later on we'd meet again at the apartment and lie around in bed watching the "Late Show" or Steve Allen, who had the big late-night talk show at the time, and after we'd screw around until we fell asleep. The situation with my sisters didn't get any better, and the fact that some of the columnists got wind of our private little family fight, and that Brace and I were living in the same hotel, didn't exactly help. "Brandi on the Rocks"—that was the headline on one item, and that just about described it.

It was just about at this time that we played a week of one-night stands with Freddie Manners. Brace had been called to the coast to reshoot some scenes from his last picture, and he was going to be gone about three weeks, so I was glad to have the tour come along, despite the one-sided feud that Freddie was carrying on with me.

When Freddie does a thing, he does it in a big splashy way. In the old days, one-night stands called for long, uncomfortable rides on trains or buses. You'd do the show, then pile into a bus or a day coach and sit up all night sleeping the best you could, traveling for maybe ten, twelve hours to the next town where you were on the bill. Then you'd rehearse the show, do it, get back into the bus, and on you went. Freddie did his one-nighters in his own private railroad cars. That's right, plural. Three, count 'em, three. A sleeper, a diner, and a private car for Freddie which was fitted out with a lot of gadgets to amuse the great comic, including a few female ones.

For the whole tour, Freddie didn't talk to me. If I wanted to ask him a question, he would turn away and say, "Ask Dorey. Leave me alone." His pride was still hurt.

On the last day of the tour, the four of us were called to his private compartment just before we pulled into Detroit, where we were going to play the final show. By this time I was really fed up with him. I didn't want to see him at all but my sisters insisted because he might be offended if I didn't show up, and after all, we couldn't afford to offend Freddie Manners, right? So we all went to see him.

When we got to his private car, he was sitting in his special lounge chair which, I was told, could flip back and make a bed with a motor underneath that bounced him up and down in the right place so he could bang the girl on top without having to move himself.

Anyhow, he had us line up in front of him and then he said, "We're coming in to Detroit this afternoon so we can have plenty of time to get ready for the show tonight. I want you girls to look really sharp for this last show."

He snapped his fingers and one of his boys handed him a roll of hundred-dollar bills. He peeled off eight and handed each of us two. I was the Grandma of the act, so my sisters looked at me like they didn't understand. Neither did I.

"What's this for?" I asked.

"I'm not talking to her," Freddie snapped. Then he

turned to my sisters and he said, "I want you to go out and buy yourselves beautiful outfits and come and show Sam." Sam was his stage manager and chief ass-licker.

His attitude really bugged me, and anyhow I don't like things happening like money being thrown around outside of the contract. Besides, after Jerry and Bob Ford and Brace, I was taking no shit from any man.

"I don't think we should take this," I said.

"Tell her to take it," he told Angie. "And tell her to keep her mouth shut. All she wants to do is spar with me. I don't spar with dames."

We went shopping in Detroit with Freddie's money; I bought myself a beaded cashmere sweater with pearls and a pair of slacks to match. That was my two hundred dollars' worth, right? Then we went back to the train, put on our new clothes, and showed them to Sam, who smiled and nodded and said, "Fine."

The Detroit show went like a rocket. It was a wonderful windup to what had been, in spite of Freddie, a very successful tour; the press was there, and television coverage, the works.

A few days after we got back to New York, our manager, Sol Leonard, called me up.

"Oh, you kids, you're driving me nuts," he says. "What's the matter with you kids? You're getting me into trouble every day."

"What happened, Solly? What's the matter?"

"I just got the worst letter I ever got in my life," he says. "Registered special delivery. From Freddie Manners. From Freddie Manners to his lawyers to me."

I couldn't believe my ears.

"But we did great on the show!" I said. "We knocked them dead at every performance. What are you talking about, Sol?"

Solly read me the letter. I remember it so well, I can quote it almost word for word.

"Tell the four fucking finks to give me back my eight hundred dollars. My accountants have to make up my books and they don't balance. If they don't give me back the money, I'll sue them in court."

He didn't sue because Solly handled it for us and explained the thing to the accountants, which was just as well, because by the next day I wouldn't have had the head to manage, anyhow. When I woke up that morning I realized that I was four days late.

I waited another week but nothing happened, so I

picked up my sinking stomach and went to see a doctor. He took a couple of tests, and gave me the news. I was pregnant. I told the doctor I wasn't married and that my boyfriend was in California, and he told me not to wait any more than four or five weeks at the latest if I was going to do anything about it.

I went back to the apartment in a daze, and I thought back to our first time in Brooklyn and realized that he hadn't done anything to protect me. This was before the pill, remember. Then the feeling came over me of how alone I really was, because I couldn't go to my mother or sisters.

I called him that night, wanting to talk to him in the worst way, but before I could tell him anything, he told me he was off on a State Department cultural exchange tour, and what a big honor it was for him to be included, and if I didn't have to sing with my sisters I could come along with him.

When he was finished telling me the whole exciting story, I said, "Let me give you my news in a nutshell, Brace. I'm pregnant."

You could have heard a bad joke laying an egg over three thousand miles of telephone wire, it was that quiet, only this was an egg without a joke.

"It can't be!" he said when he could finally speak.

"Oh, yes it can," I told him. "Just think back to Brooklyn and you'll see."

"Oh, my God!" he moaned. "What am I going to do?"

"What are you going to do?" I almost hit the ceiling. "What am I going to do! The doctor says I can't wait more than a couple of weeks."

"Doctor! What doctor? What does he know? Don't listen to his bullshit!"

"Why, have you been through this before?"

By this time I was so hurt by his whole attitude that I couldn't lose a chance to stick in a few pins where I thought they might hurt back.

"No, but I've got friends who have," he said in a soothing tone of voice. "This happens to a lot of people. So what? Listen, you can wait another three or four weeks. Look, I'll be back by then and I'll write you in the meantime every day. Or at least I'll try, because we'll be traveling almost every day. I've got to get off the phone now because I've got a lot of thinking to do."

"So have I!" I said, and hung up because by now I was feeling a little sick and nauseous and I had to lie down.

My morale was lower than before I had called him, and I said out loud, "Dear God, I can't go through this alone. I just can't. He's got to come back. He's got to!"

The phone rang. It was Angie telling me about the next day's rehearsal, and that we had a two-day date singing at a club for a charity drive. I said all right, just as though everything was, and I hung up and cried for a couple of hours.

Can you believe all this? Doesn't it sound like a daytime soap? Honest to God, I should be writing television scripts based on my own life, right? "Life Can Be Messy," originated, produced, directed, written by Nina Brandi and starring Nina Brandi, all the way.

The next week was a bad dream. I went to rehearsals and I sang the shows and every night I felt deathly ill and dizzy, and in between shows I had to rush to the bathroom to vomit. My sisters forgot their mad temporarily and wanted to call a doctor, but I wouldn't let them because of my pride. I didn't want them to know the kind of fix I was in, even though I'm sure they suspected. Hell, how could they not!

By the end of the week there was one postcard from Brace, just one. A picture of some goddamn statue of some guy on a horse somewhere in Poland was just what I needed! That night we were doing the first of those two nights of benefits and Angie called up to say that she would stop by and pick me up. She was worried about me, and since she knew that Brace was away she was sort of keeping an eye on me without telling the rest of the family. I took my usual shower and I was getting dressed in the bathroom when I looked down and there was a pool of blood on the floor. I knew right away that I was hemorrhaging, but there was no doctor in the hotel; I panicked so bad I couldn't remember the name of the doctor I had gone to. I lay down on the bed to wait for Angie, keeping my feet up like they say you should. By the time she knocked at the door, I was so weak I had to crawl to the door to let her in. She took one look and got on the phone and I heard her talking to the desk, asking for a doctor in a hurry, and then I blacked out. When I came to, there was a doctor standing over me giving me a needle and telling Angie that I was six weeks' pregnant.

The doctor wanted me to stay in bed but we had a benefit to sing and we were committed, so I had Angie pay him and get him out. After he left, Angie sat down on the bed and said, "Oh, Nina, no! Not my little sister!"

"Now, look, Angie," I told her, "no sermons, please. I'm old enough to take care of myself."

"And where the hell is he? Does he know?"

"He knows. And he'll be back—I think!" I couldn't sound as optimistic as I wanted to so I couldn't keep back that "I think."

Angie helped me to dress and we got into a cab and drove to the club. As soon as we got there I sat down backstage, and when they announced us I went out on-stage with my sisters and we sang our numbers.

It was like when we were kids singing those dates where Marcie and I had to stay hidden because we were under-age and Pop could have been arrested for the child labor laws or something. He used to say that we were midgets if anyone saw us, and the guy would look at him like he didn't believe it and laugh. It was always our luck that we didn't go on until maybe eleven or twelve o'clock at night and we had to be there at about seven-thirty, so all that time we had to stay in the dressing room where no one could see us. We were little kids then. I was seven or eight and Marcie was only a year or so older, so we used to have to fight to stay awake. Sometimes Pop would come in and find me leaning up against Marcie and the both of us asleep or dozing off, and he would shake us awake and yell at us. And quite a few times, my nose would start to bleed for some unknown reason. I could feel it getting stuffy, like I was getting a cold, and all of a sudden little red drops would fall onto my hands and Marcie would stick her head out the door and send someone to find Pop. He would come rushing in and make me put my head back so I didn't get blood on my dress and he would take Kleenex and stuff it up my nose. It didn't make any difference as far as my singing went because I have a nasal voice as is and a little more "nose," as my father called it, wasn't even noticed. Of course, I felt like hell out there onstage because I had to keep smiling and singing with my nose stuffed with Kleenex and the blood running down the back of my throat, which made me want to swallow so bad, but I used to hang on and go through the whole act that way.

There's no business like, isn't that what the song says!

That was how I felt that night, singing at the benefit, and hanging on. After we took our bows, I got right back in the cab which was waiting there and went back to the apartment and back to bed. The doctor had left me some pills, which I took, and when I got up the next morning I felt much better. I didn't lose the baby after all, which wasn't such a good thing because it would have saved me a lot of grief and pain if I had.

Brace called a couple of days later. He was back in Hollywood after the end of the tour and he was having all kinds of trouble with the divorce business. He called me up two or three times to tell me about it, and he sounded really frantic.

"Please, honey," he pleaded over the phone, "just let me get myself straightened out and I promise you I'll be back and everything will be all right."

What could I say?

"All right, Brace," I told him. "I have to trust you because you're all I have."

"That's the way I want it," he said, and that was the way it was, like it or not.

Then we had to play a date in Moline at a new, very swanky club in one of those hotels that cater to conventions, which they have a lot of in Moline because it's so close to Chicago without actually being in the city. By this time my system had settled down and I was over being sick, so my sisters weren't talking to me again. I had to go to Moline by myself on the train, and all the way there I sat up in the day coach thinking about how different and lonely it was going out of town to play a date traveling without my sisters, and how in a couple of weeks I would have to face an abortion without anyone from my family standing by. I also had to face up to the fact that I was beginning to feel something for this little thing growing inside me, and by the time I got to Moline, you can imagine the state of mind I was in.

The Moline date went fine, but the atmosphere backstage was deadly. Onstage we were still the Four Brandi Sisters, laughing together and smiling and singing, and the audience loved us the way they always did. But as soon as we got offstage, the wall came down and I was locked out again. Angie looked very sorry about it and sometimes I would catch her looking at me with pity in her eyes. Not the others. If they looked in my direction at all, which was not very often, their eyes slid right over me and off into space. I was not trying to make it up with them, either, I can tell you. I had the weight of the world on my shoulders with the baby growing inside my stomach and the idea that my life was in the worst mess ever growing inside my head, but I wasn't going to let them see that, no sir! I got up on my high horse and looked right at and through them, and when I was finished changing in the dressing room after the show, out I went and up to my room and I sat alone there watching television, stewing inside.

At the end of the week, I went to the management as usual to collect our pay because I was still the Grandma of the act, only someone had been there before me. When I got back to the dressing room, there was the money all divided up but there was none for me. Dolores said I owed the act a lot of money and we had a big fight about it until finally I threatened to quit.

Then Marcie said to me, "To be honest with you, Nina, we'd feel a lot better if you did. The act would have a cleaner reputation."

Now that was a helluva thing for her to say because, after all, I was the Patty Andrews and the Harry Ritz of the act. Most of the routines were built around me. I thought of all that during that stunned minute of silence. But the bitterness and hurt blocked it out and I told her, "You couldn't have said it more clearly. That's fine with me. Keep the money because you'll never see me again." I picked up my makeup kit and my purse, crying like mad all the time, and walked out and went back up to my room.

I sat around for a day thinking about how I had been with the act since I was five years old and how much we had gone through with Pop and the fun we had on the road and the hardships and the tears, playing the Borscht Belt and all, and how it had all blown up in my face. They say that if you're in show business long enough, everything that can happen happens to you, and now it seemed as if the worst thing of all had happened to me. I called Brace and told him, and would you believe it, he came flying right out from L.A. to Moline? I guess breaking up the act, and the money, were more important than my being pregnant, because when I had told him about the baby he went right on with his cultural exchange tour, right?

Anyhow, he wanted me to try to patch things up with my sisters, but I was too hurt by what Marcie had said and I wasn't giving in for nothing, so I packed my things and we went back to New York. As soon as we were back in the apartment, Brace started to make plans for the abortion. It was like an old OSS movie with him making mysterious phone calls and phone calls coming back and everything that was said was just circling all around what we were really talking about, if you know what I mean.

This went on for a week and I sat there listening to it all, knowing that plans were being made to kill my baby, because that's how I felt about the poor little thing by then.

The night before it was supposed to be done, I said, "Brace, is there any chance that I can have this baby?"

"Honey," he said, "I'd give anything if you could have my child, but there's the divorce. I'm getting a Reno decree soon and then the California divorce will come through a year from the day that happens, and if anything like this baby gets to be known, the scandal could kill the whole thing."

I started to cry and he said, "Now, look, Nina. You know you're not the first girl to go through a thing like this and you won't be the last."

"But I've been pregnant so long, I feel that whatever is inside me is mine and I don't want to give it up."

"I'm sorry, honey, but it just isn't possible," and the way he said it I could tell that he really didn't want the baby, no matter what he said.

The next night we took a cab to a residential hotel near Fifth Avenue. We went in through an archway off the street and into a courtyard with old-fashioned street lamps all around. It was like a set for the picture "Gaslight," only it was more gloomy instead of scary. The doctor had his office in this hotel and Brace had rented a room for us a couple of floors above because I was supposed to get out of the doctor's office under my own power as soon as it was over and Brace didn't want to take a chance on getting me back to the apartment. We got into the hotel through a side door and then we went down a corridor and in through a kitchen door into this apartment which was also the doctor's office. We didn't actually go into the office but I got a look at it when the doctor came into the kitchen. He was a little gray-haired man of about sixty, and he was very nervous all the time he was talking to us. He got up a dozen times to open the kitchen door to make sure no one was there, and once or twice he looked out of the window into the street, I guess to see if anybody had followed us or something. It was all very OSS.

He said he would have to examine me, which he did in a little bedroom off the kitchen, probably a maid's room at one time because it had a daybed and a chair. That examination was the roughest, crudest thing I ever went through. I didn't undress, of course, and there was no nurse, just me on this daybed and the doctor poking around inside while I held my skirt up out of the way.

Finally we went back into the kitchen, and he said, "I don't think I can do it. You're almost twelve weeks pregnant."

"That's impossible," I told him. "I've got the time all figured out."

"Look, I'm the doctor," he told me. "Your uterus shows a twelve-week pregnancy, believe me, and that's very dangerous. You know you could lose her because she could hemorrhage to death," he said to Brace. "I don't think I can touch it. It's too dangerous."

"Your fee is a thousand, isn't it?" Brace said to him. "In cash?"

"That's right," the doctor said. "But I still won't touch it. She would have to stay here for a couple of *hours* so I could make sure she wasn't hemorrhaging. It's too risky."

Brace took out his billfold and started to count out hundred-dollar bills, and when he was finished there were fifteen of them on the kitchen table. I could see the doctor counting with him, not out loud but with his lips moving without a sound and his eyes on the money. When Brace was finished, he said, "All right, let's get going."

I was wearing a suit, and when I got up to take off my jacket, the doctor said, "No, no, no! Stay completely dressed, please!"

I looked at Brace and he said, "Just go along with him, please, honey."

The doctor and I went back into the little room and I lay down again on the bed and he went to work. He did do one thing for me. He gave me some kind of shot that half knocked me out so I didn't feel too much pain. I remember looking at my watch as I lay down and then came the needle and I was half asleep. The watch stayed in my mind even with the pain, and when I came to I looked at it again and it was two and a half hours later. I must have been crying because my eyes were wet, and when I looked up at the doctor he looked all blurry and I heard him say, "It was a little boy."

When I heard that, everything seemed to let go inside me, all the tension and the fear and worry of all those weeks waiting for this thing to happen, and it bore down on me so I had to let it out.

"Get out of here!" I screamed at him. "Get out, you lousy butcher! Is that what you do, you tell the mother the sex of the child? I don't want to know! I don't want to

91

know!" I started to cry hysterically and Brace came in and held me and the doctor was saying, "You've got to get her out of here right away. She stayed too long already."

"I'll get the elevator," Brace said, and he went out by the back door. After he was gone, the doctor looked at me and said, "If you wanted this baby so much and you were so concerned about what was going to happen to you, why didn't you make Jerry Miller marry you?"

For a minute I didn't know what he was saying. I couldn't understand it. It didn't make any sense.

"What did you say?" I asked him.

"Mr. Fontaine told me all about your troubles. You seem like such a wonderful girl. Why didn't Mr. Miller marry you?"

The words sank in and I stared at him. I was really stunned. Then Brace came back and I looked at him, and he must have seen a funny expression on my face because he said, "What's the matter?"

I should have said what I was thinking: "The matter is I'm seeing you for the first time, you bastard!" Instead I didn't say a word. I just got myself together and he helped me up and we started out. The doctor pressed a roll of bandage into my hands and told me to change the packing the next day and I walked slowly out into the hallway and into the automatic service elevator that Brace had waiting with a rolled-up newspaper in the door and we went up to our floor.

When we got to our room, he helped me undress and I don't know to this day whether I imagined it or not because I really wasn't all there yet, but it seemed as though he acted like he was getting me ready to make love. He kept putting his hands all over me as the clothes came off, and when I stepped out of my panties, painfully, one foot at a time, and he bent down to get them, his face brushed against my crotch and I could have sworn he tried to press his face in for a second.

I had sleeping pills with me, which I took, but even so it took me a long time to get to sleep, and then I didn't sleep too well because all the pills did was make me drowsy. We were in a double bed and I wished to hell that Brace had gotten a room with singles instead because I didn't feel like having anybody close to me that night. The shot wore off and I started feeling some pain and, of course, I was still bleeding and very weak and in shock. I lay there in a kind of half-sleep and once in a while I would doze off and dream. I kept thinking that I could feel Brace's hands on me, and once I thought I felt him getting on top of me because I woke myself up saying out loud, "No, no! Please, leave me alone!" and I half sat up, but he was lying next to me and not moving. I put my hands down to check the packing and I could feel that it was coming out, so I went to the bathroom to fix it. Half of it was out and I put it back in the best I could and went back to bed. Brace was lying there with his eyes closed and for a minute I wondered if he was really asleep because he didn't seem to be breathing very heavily, but I was too exhausted to care, so I lay back down and drifted off again. I woke up once again and I was saying "Jerry Miller . . . Jerry Miller" over and over again to myself. And then I remember saying to myself, very sleepy-like, "That's what the sonofabitch told him . . . he told him that . . ."

Chapter
NINE

The next day we went back to the apartment and I lay around for two or three days until I finally stopped bleeding and things started getting back to normal. I felt as though everything had been taken out of me, all my emotions and feelings, just everything, as though I didn't have any will to do anything with my life anymore. If someone had told me that I was dying and it was only a matter of days or even hours, I don't think I would have had any regrets. Once in a while Jackie came over to me and licked my hand and I petted him a little, and that was about all the attention I paid to anything around me.

For the first couple of days Brace was very thoughtful and paid me a lot of attention. He brought me food and ice water and propped pillows under my head, but when he wanted to change the packing I wouldn't let him, and I made such a fuss that he dropped the idea fast. I thought he was trying to be helpful but some of those dreams or whatever they were that had bothered me the night of the abortion stuck in my head, and the thought of him even touching me there was just too much. In fact, I didn't want him around me. I didn't want anybody there, I guess, though if my mother had come walking in I would have welcomed her with open arms. It was not just Brace. I felt that I didn't want to have anything to do with men, period, not any of them ever again, and if I had read a headline in the newspaper saying that every man in the world had dropped dead, I think I would have cheered.

I got back my strength gradually over the next three or four weeks, and during all that time Brace and I didn't have much to say to each other. I think that if I had had any money of my own and still had an act to sing with I would have left him right then and there, but there was no one else and I was flat broke, so what could I do?

Worst of all was the way the abortion haunted me. I couldn't get it out of my mind and I kept reliving the whole rotten business and how I wanted to keep the baby at the end and not get rid of it. I even had a name all picked out if it was a boy. Christopher. I would have called him Christopher.

I know a number of girls who have had abortions; most of them just seemed to throw it off like it was no worse than having a tooth pulled, but not me. I'm not built that way. I knew then that it would bug me for the rest of my life.

The business about marrying Brace and making the marriage work didn't seem so important anymore. I still had in my mind how he lied to the doctor and told him the baby was Jerry's, and I knew I would never forget that and that I'd never forgive him for it, either. I just didn't see how I could marry him after that. There didn't seem to be anything left of our relationship, and I think he felt the same way, too.

We didn't talk much to each other and he was out of the apartment a lot and left me alone for hours and then days. No sex, of course, not while I was getting over the abortion, and not even after that because I just couldn't stand the idea of having a man touch me or come into me or anything. Of course, that was pretty bad for Brace because for him it was like a man dying of thirst looking at a glass of water behind a glass screen that he can't get through. I didn't know what he was doing to make up for it and I didn't care, so when he told me that he had to go to the coast to reshoot some scenes in his picture, I was relieved and looked forward to being alone.

Before he went I made him drive me out to Brooklyn so I could pick up my clothes that were still there. I called Mom and told her I was coming, and when she said she would be out and to help myself, that was the first time I had any feeling of emotion since the abortion. I would have liked to have seen her again and maybe make up with her. When we got there she was out, like she said she would be. We went into the empty house and I packed up my stuff and looked around at what had once been my home, and took a last look at the kitchen where my world had come unstuck, and then we went back to our hotel apartment. Jesus, God, the things people do to each other even when they love each other! . . . You've got the right idea, friend. No feelings, no emotions, just a lot of transistors and wires and knobs. That's the way we should all be.

Talking to Mom and going back to Brooklyn was probably just the emotional shock I needed to get me off dead center, because I started to think about myself again in a positive way. I decided that I had had enough of sitting around on my ass and feeling sorry for myself and that what I should do was get back into show business with my own act. As soon as Brace left, I got busy on the phone calling up every agent in town. By this time the final chapter of the Brandi Sisters was being written. There had been items in the columns and a big story in *Variety*, and one in *Billboard*, that went through our whole history, and the general opinion around the business was that it was a damn shame to break up such a good act.

That was what the agents said when I spoke to them, and I agreed, and we talked about how long it takes to build up an act and make it go and how much tougher the business was now than when we got started. Then I would tell them my idea about a solo act and they would say that solos are hard to sell, and finally they would end by giving me the old don't-call-us-we'll-call-you routine. This went on for almost a week until I finally called Mike Krantz. At that time Mike was a music publisher as well as an agent. I had dated him a couple of times back in the Jerry Miller days. We had had a thing for a month or so, but now when I called him up and told him my idea he was all business, and he flipped.

"Nina, I think that you as a single would be out of this world. It's only great," was the way he put it. The next morning I was in his office signing a contract with him as my manager and he got me together with a couple of arrangers, and by the time the week was over I was working up my own act. At first my heart wasn't in it completely. It was a real twist for me even to think of working alone, and when I actually started putting songs and material together I found myself thinking in terms of four, not one. But I did it. I put my nose to the old grindstone and worked ten hours a day to get it done. I had been doing a lot of thinking about my future in the business and about my life with Brace, and I had come to the conclusion that I had to make this work. I didn't have my mother and sisters on my side anymore. There was no more act, so I couldn't earn my own money. I was completely dependent on Brace, who was paying the rent and footing all the bills, right? And he wasn't free to marry me, so that little bell in my head was going *ting! ting!* working overtime because Jerry was always in the back of my head, still sneaking around there to remind me of what could happen. I needed the insurance of being able to go out on my own. I may have been pretty naïve about a lot of things at that time, but I had a strong instinct to survive on my own and I was playing it for all it was worth.

The day before Brace got back to New York, Mike called up to tell me that he had just gotten me my first booking. It was in Miami, where I had worked a million times with my sisters, but the thought of going there by myself scared me to death.

Mike was a big, burly man with graying hair at the temples and a face that had been beaten up when he was a boxer in the navy. He had a very hearty manner and he was just what I needed at the time, because he knew just how to bolster my ego and keep up my morale. "Of course you're frightened," he told me. "You'll be frightened the first couple of times when you're standing up there alone because you've never done it before. It's only natural. But you can do it, Nina. I know you can. I wouldn't be going through all this if I didn't think so."

"What hotel did you get?" I asked him, and when he told me the Saxony, I felt more than scared. I was really in a panic.

"Mike, the Saxony!" I said, with butterflies racing all over my stomach. "Couldn't you have broken me in in a smaller place?"

"Don't be silly," he said. "Listen, everybody and his brother is going to be there to see you, Ed Sullivan, everybody. You'll take off like a rocket!"

"Or blow up like a bomb," I told him. "All right, Mike, the Saxony it is. I've been in this business since I was five years old, so I guess I might as well go for broke."

"That's the spirit!" he said. "And listen, you'll be playing with a great guy, so you should get a lot of help from him. They've got a real star on the bill with you, honey, so don't feel you have to carry this all by yourself."

He told me that he was talking about Mickey Faye, and that cleared away the last doubts. I felt I had to play that date. Mickey was coming up to the height of his career then. He already had his own hour television show which was building up a great rating, and everybody knew he was a real comer, so sharing a bill with him was a real break for a new act. And when everybody told me he was so great to work with, I couldn't wait to get down to Miami.

Brace flew in the next day. I went to meet him at the airport. When he came through the gate I saw he wasn't alone. Joye and Sam Garrick were with him and there were kisses all around when we said hello, and Brace picked me up and whirled me around right there in the terminal building he was so glad to see me. In the cab on the way into town, I didn't have a chance to tell Brace about the new act because he was busy telling me about the reshooting, and Joye and Sam were full of their plans. They were moving into New York for a while. They wanted to produce a couple of features in New York, but so far they hadn't been able to find the right scripts, so Joye was going to write them herself. In fact, Sam had a lot of contacts in the book business, so they had figured out that if the films were written as books first and if the books were successful, then the pictures would make a lot more money. Joye was going to write the books and then Sam was going to promote them and then they'd do them as features. And while they were living in New York they were going to take us everywhere, to all the good places, and introduce Brace to the right people so he could move in on television and take it over.

We dropped the Garricks off at the Plaza and got back to our own place, and Brace couldn't wait to get my clothes off. As he was undressing me he was telling me how much he had missed me and how much he loved me, and by the time we got onto the bed he had his head in between my legs already and was going to town. This was the first time we had had sex since before the abortion and he kept at me for hours, I don't remember how long, until finally I had to beg him to stop and give me a rest. Then, while we were lying on the bed resting, I was finally able to talk to him.

I told him about the act and what the booking was like and about being on the same bill with Mickey Faye. I showed how excited I really was about it, and I guess he saw that as some kind of threat, because by the time I was finished he didn't look too happy.

"Why do you need all that?" he wanted to know. "After all, I have all the money in the world."

I didn't want to tell him that I wanted to make myself independent, just in case, so I said, "But Brace, I have people to answer to now."

"Who?" he wanted to know, so I told him about Mike Krantz.

"Who's he, one of your ex-boyfriends?"

"He was but he's just a friend, now."

He got very huffy about that.

"Go ahead, keep talking," he said, jumping off the bed and lighting a cigarette. "You're just burying yourself."

"I'm not burying myself," I told him, starting to get a little huffy myself. "I don't have to answer to you. We may be going together and living together like this, but we're not really engaged or anything. Just pre-engaged, remember? After all, you're not exactly a free man, right? So don't try to tell me what to do with my life. I'm not even sure I want to go on living with you, even if we could get married, especially if you're going to act like this and try to tie me down."

That took some of the wind out of his sails because he started to look worried and sad and told me again all about how much he had missed me and how as soon as he got back and we were together again we were fighting and so on.

That made me feel kind of sorry for him, because he did seem to be so much in love with me, so I said, "Look Brace, just let me get this out of my system. Let me try the act, just to see if I can make it on my own as an entertainer, all right?"

"Fine! You do that!" he said, mad again. "I've been offered the International Cafe for six weeks, so I think I'll take that while you traipse around the country on your own, all right?"

"I can always move out," I told him, and that stopped him again. He saw that I meant it, so he got back on the bed and said, "Come over here, sorehead," and we had sex again for another couple of hours. He really went down on me, sucking and chewing away and making me come again and again and again until I thought I would scream. Finally he let me go and I staggered into the bathroom to recover. I sat there thinking about him and how violent he had gotten all of a sudden in my mother's house and how he was getting more and more perverted in bed, and I had the feeling that putting the act over was maybe more important to me than I realized.

Brace signed for the International and went into rehearsal and I went into the final week of preparing my act, so we were both so tied up we didn't see much of each other that week. The night before I was to leave for Miami, he went out to a music rehearsal with his piano player and I was busy packing when the phone rang and a long-distance operator asked for me. Then a strange woman's voice came on and said, "Is this Nina Brandi?"

I said, "Yes, who is this?"

She said, "This is Selma Fontaine."

I almost dropped the phone. What do you say when your boyfriend's ex-wife calls you up out of a clear blue sky?

I needed time to think so I said, "How do you do? How are you?"

"I have to explain," she said. "I have pretty good detectives and they found out where you and Brace are living. That's how I was able to get your phone number."

"If that's what you want," I told her, "why don't you handle this through your lawyers? Or through Brace's lawyers? Why talk to me?"

"Honey," she said, "I'm not calling up for that. The way the divorce is going, I don't need an adultery charge on Brace. I'm calling you because I want to save you from a terrible life if I can."

"Now, wait a minute, Selma," I said. "This isn't the scorned wife talking, is it?"

"Believe me, it isn't. And if I didn't know that you are a really nice girl and that you come from a decent family, I wouldn't bother. If you were that blond dyke he was sleeping with in Las Vegas, I wouldn't give it a second thought."

"You mean that blonde gofer of his?"

"That's the one. My detectives were out there, too. She's bisexual. She was making it with the captain of the line when she was sleeping with Brace, how do you like that?"

"What's all that got to do with me?"

"Well, I thought you should know, before you tie yourself down to this guy, that he's bisexual too."

I looked at the receiver in my hand trying to decide whether or not to hang up, and I heard her say, "Nina!

Nina, are you there? Nina, answer me. Don't hang up, please. Just hear me out."

"All right," I said putting the receiver back to my ear. "But you'd better have proof."

"I have," she said. "In writing. Listen, I went through this with him for fifteen years. He went to a psychiatrist and the psychiatrist told me it's in his system and there's nothing anyone can do about it. And I tried, God knows, I tried. For fifteen years. Listen, he may be acting completely straight in bed now, but sooner or later, he'll go back. They always do."

"How do I know that all this is true?" I said, my head whirling around. "What kind of proof do you have?"

"I've got a letter," she said. "We have a mutual friend, a composer out here, who's a homosexual, and he and Brace have had an affair. I can show you a letter that this friend wrote to Brace, a real love letter from one man to another. It even describes their bed routine. Do you want me to mail it to you?"

"No, no. Please don't. I believe that you have a letter. Look, I have to hang up now. I'm opening a new act tomorrow in Miami and you've upset me very much. You couldn't have called at a worse time."

"Yes, I can see that," she said. "I am sorry, but I just had to let you know before it was too late. If I can save you from what I went through, then it was worth upsetting you."

"I have to think now," I told her. "Good-bye," and I hung up.

I thought and I thought and I thought some more. Then I had a drink of scotch, which is something unusual for me to do because, as you know, I hardly ever drink. Only when I'm about to be raped or when I've just been told my husband-to-be is gay. I'm sure you've noticed that about me. I sat by the phone drinking my scotch slowly, waiting for Brace to come home, thinking, What the hell have I got myself into? Can I believe her? I'll ask Brace and if he denies it, can I believe him? I thought about Bob Ford and how he had surprised me and about how Brace was different in bed than other men, but that didn't prove anything, either, at least not to me it didn't.

Brace walked in at about two in the morning and found me still sitting by the phone, still with a drink in my hand, because I had poured myself another. It was a two-scotch crisis, and though I didn't know it yet, it was about to become a full quart emergency. God, how can I make jokes about this? Oh well! Maybe it's good that I can.

"Hi, baby," he said. "What's up?"

"Sit down, Brace," I said. "I want to talk to you."

"OK," he said, sitting down. "Only not for too long, huh? You're going off deserting me tomorrow, so I'd like to get to bed with you one more time, OK? What's the matter? Is everything all right?"

"Everything's fine. I just want to talk to you," I said, not knowing how to start.

"You have the strangest look on your face," he said. "It's been a long day and I've been working goddamn hard all night and I come back to a puss like that. What's up?"

"I had a call tonight."

"Must have been some call. Who from?"

"Your wife, Selma."

He sat up when he heard that.

"She called here? How'd she get the number?"

"She's got detectives on our trail. She knows where we've been living, our number, everything."

"Well, that's nothing to worry about," he said, relaxing again. "I've got five lawyers working on the divorce and she's only getting what I want to give her, so don't let it bother you. Come on, let's go to bed, baby. Never mind about her."

"No, wait," I said. "There was more to it than that. That's not what she called about."

"Well, for Christ's sake, let's hear it already."

"I don't know how to tell you this," I said. "Not without you getting upset."

"Honey," he said, "I won't ever get upset with you because I love you too much."

"All right," I said. "Here it is. Your wife told me that you are a homosexual."

He sat there looking at me and his face didn't change, not a muscle.

"Did you believe it?" he asked.

I looked back up at him and I said, "She told me about some composer friend and about a letter he wrote you."

"Do you believe it?" he said.

He wasn't saying yes or no. He wasn't denying or even trying to explain, nothing, and I felt I needed some answers but I wasn't getting any.

"Well, suppose I ask her for this fictitious letter," I said, trying to sound reasonable and not suspicious. "I mean if

101

somebody is writing letters like that about you, don't you think we should—"

As I was talking I saw him get up and walk over to me and then the lights went out. That's the only way I can describe what happened. Everything turned off all around me. The next thing I knew I was lying in bed and there was a doctor standing over me next to Brace and saying, "I think she's coming around. Get some water."

I started to say, "What happened?" but when I moved my mouth to talk it hurt like hell and my lips felt all puffed up and sore. Then they were giving me water and I looked up at them and said, "What happened?"

"It's all right, Miss Brandi," the doctor said. "Just lie there quietly because you've had quite a fall."

I looked at him like he was crazy or I was crazy because the last thing I remembered was talking to Brace and I didn't remember any fall.

"What fall?" I said. "What's the matter with me? Why does my mouth feel like this?"

"Just relax," he said. "Take it easy. I had to give you a couple of stitches. You're just going through a little shock now so just lie back and relax."

Stitches! I thought. My God, my opening!

"I want to get up," I said, starting to swing my legs over the side of the bed.

"Now please, Miss Brandi," he said, trying to hold me down.

"Leave me alone," I said, pushing him away, and I jumped out of bed and ran into the bathroom to look in the mirror. I couldn't believe what I saw. My mouth was five times its normal size and my bottom lip was badly cut. I could see the dried blood and the stitches.

"My God!" I said. "My mouth ... my mouth ... my lip."

"You'll be all right," the doctor said behind me. "It's just a few stitches."

I turned around and looked at him and behind him I saw Brace watching me and I said, "I want to get out of here."

"Take it easy, Miss Brandi," the stupid doctor said. "I've given you a sedative so you should lie down and take it easy. Your fiancé will take care of you."

"Fiancé!" I said.

"Yes, he found you on the bathroom floor. You obviously can't hold your liquor very well, can you, Miss Brandi?"

102

"Look, Doctor," I said. "I have to get to a—to my hotel. I need a good night's rest because I'm opening in Miami tomorrow night."

"Don't worry about that," he said. "The stitches are in the corner of your lip so they won't be seen. You'll be all right. We're going to put ice packs on it now and your fiancé will put them on every two hours and by tomorrow you'll be fine again. You really should stay here and relax. You've had a sudden shock and you should not be wandering around by yourself. Let him take care of you tonight."

Then he turned to Brace, took his money, and left.

As he was walking him to the door, I heard Brace say, "Thanks a million, Doctor. I didn't know what to do. I really panicked when I found her."

That sonofabitch, I thought to myself. I never met anybody like him in my life! I'm getting out of here!

Brace came back and said to me, "Now look, Nina. I can explain."

"Explain!" I said to him with my mouth hurting like hell while I talked. "How do you explain this? What's the matter with you? You must be gay if you got so upset over what happened."

"Now look," he said. "Don't get me started on you again, please."

"What the hell are you, a woman-beater?" I said. "Is this the guy I met in Las Vegas? The one who was going to knock Jerry Miller on his ass because he smacked me in the face? The guy who was going to kill him for it?"

"Nina, I never hit a woman before in my life. You drove me to it."

"Drove you!" I almost screamed the words. "Drove you? What did I do? I repeated what your wife said to me! What is wrong with that?"

"You had skepticism in your voice," he said. "I thought you believed her."

"So what kind of an excuse is that—"

"No, wait, Nina," he cut in. "Look, let me get the ice packs before you say another word. You've got to get that mouth down to normal size by tomorrow morning."

I was feeling kind of woozy so I lay back down and he brought in ice packs and put them on and he gave me some water to drink when I said my mouth burned inside. I looked at him and said, "I can't believe it. Even that sock from Jerry was not this bad. Stitches! My God! My father, an immigrant from Italy, never hit us so bad we had to have stitches."

"I just went out of my head," he said, sounding very low and sorry. "You were asking me about this letter and there's no such thing as any letter and that goddamned cunt is so jealous of you—!"

"I don't want to hear any more!" I told him. "All I know is this fat lip. Look at me! What am I going to do?"

"I'll take care of it," he said. "I'll fly down with you tomorrow for your opening, and everything's going to be—"

"The hell you will!" I yelled at him. "You're not flying anywhere with me. You're not going to louse up all the work I've put into the act. I'm going down there with my manager."

"Have it your own way," he said.

"And how!" I said. "Now give me the ice packs. I can take care of myself."

"All right," he said. "I'm going out for a couple of hours. I need a few drinks."

"Make it an even dozen," I told him. "Make it more than a couple of hours. I don't want to see your face. And when I leave in the morning, I don't want to see you then, either."

"That's fine with me," he said. "I'll check into a health club."

"A health club!" I yelled after him. "You mean a nuthouse, don't you?" And I put the ice pack back on my lip because it was hurting like hell.

Chapter
TEN

I spent the rest of the night holding ice packs to my face and cursing myself for getting into such a fix. The swelling was all down by the morning, and when Mike Krantz called for me to take me to the airport, you would have had to look real close to see that I wasn't completely normal. My lip was still sore and tender but I had camouflaged the stitches with powder so they didn't show.

But Mike knew that something was wrong as soon as I

opened my mouth because when I talked the lip hurt and I guess I showed it.

When I told him what had happened, he said, "Honey, you've got to get away from that madman. If he did this once, he can do it again."

"You're not telling me anything I haven't told myself, Mike," I told him. "Listen, I'm going with the first guy who says hello to me nicely in Florida." And I really meant it, because that was the way I felt.

"First things first," Mike said. He was always a very practical guy and completely professional. "You've got to put all that out of your mind. I know it's easy for me to say, but you're opening a new act and you can't afford to think about anything but that."

I started unloading my worries on him. "Oh, Mike, I'm so damn unsure about the act. It's no good. It doesn't hold a candle to the Brandi Sisters."

"Forget the Brandi Sisters," he said. "You're not part of the Brandi Sisters anymore. You're Nina Brandi, Nina Brandi. Just keep saying that to yourself, because that's who you are and that's who you're going to be from now on."

I knew that he was trying to put steel up my back and I tried hard to feel confident and sure of myself, but when we got to the Saxony and I saw the lobby posted all over with pictures of me, and under my pictures it said: "Nina Brandi—A New Star On Her Own" and "Nina Brandi—Songs You'll Love." I said to myself, I just don't know how I will ever get through this. Then I walked into the rehearsal hall and the musicians all looked at me and some of them said "hi!" because they had played for the Brandi Sisters many times in Miami and I could tell from the way they were looking at each other that they were skeptical about what I could do on my own. They knew that for a new act, I was in a really tough spot. In spite of what Mike said, I would have to hold up my end against a topnotch comic like Mickey, and there was also a dancer on the bill who was only great, and on top of all that this was the Saxony where the audiences expect nothing but top talent and they were used to getting it, too.

Mickey Faye came over to me with his long, thin face all smiles and he greeted me and kissed me on the cheek and said, "Glad to have you with us, Nina. I've heard a lot about you and I've seen you with your sisters, and I know you're going to be great."

I could have kissed him for that. While the band was

105

getting ready and I was looking over my music, I had a chance to ask for a glass of water and I took one of the pills the doctor had left with me the night before. I don't know what was in it, but it sure was great because in about two minutes I forgot my sore lip and I felt like nothing would ever bother me again in my whole life.

I rehearsed with the band for about three hours, which I really needed because back in New York I had only rehearsed with a piano player and had never had a chance to really hear my music. There were a lot of people out in the audience watching. The owners were sitting with Mike at one table and the publicity agent was there and there was some guy from the *Miami Daily Herald* who was supposed to do a big writeup on me, something like will-she-or-won't-she-make-it-on-her-own. It was what you would call a relaxed atmosphere, right?

The rehearsal went so-so, nothing great, and when it was over I went up to my room and slept for a couple of hours. Then before I knew it, it was two hours before show time and I was shaking like a leaf. I had given Mike the pills to hold for me and I said, "Mike, let me have another one of those pills. I think I need it."

"Not a chance," he said. "I'm not going to have you turn into a drug addict on me just because you've got an opening."

"Mike, please, after last night and everything I've been through, I really need one."

He gave it to me very reluctantly.

"It's your last one," he said, and I said, "Fine," anything to get the pill, and I took it and started feeling better right away.

"Tell me what's happening out front," I told him.

"It's great," he said. "Milton Berle is out there. And Ed Sullivan and his producer, and—"

"Oh God," I said, feeling terrible all over, pill or no pill. "What did you tell me that for?"

He took me by both arms and swung me around in front of him and said, "Now, for Christ's sake, cut it out, Nina. You're a pro, aren't you? You're going to go out there and you're going to be great, so stop worrying."

"But, Mike," I said. "That second number isn't too good, and the last number isn't a strong closer and—"

"I'm going downstairs," he said, "and I'm going to sit down at my table and I want you to come out like the professional I know you are and knock the shit out of them," and he went out and left me alone in the dressing

106

room. Half an hour before show time I got into my make-up and went backstage to watch from the wings because I couldn't stand to wait up there by myself. The curtain rang up on the opening act which was a tap dancer who milked the bejesus out of his act but he went over like he was Fred Astaire and Bill Robinson and Hal Leroy all rolled into one. Then Mickey came on and he stayed on for over an hour. The audience just would not let him go. He went through all the material in the book, everything they wanted to hear, the dirty material, the Miami Beach material, the Jewish material, and then he went into some of his well-known television routines, the ones that were favorites with his audiences, and he had that crowd in his hands. He could do no wrong. They laughed at everything he said. They even laughed when he said good night, God bless you, and went off.

That's what I followed. The big fanfare came and the emcee said, "And now, ladies and getlemen, I'm sure you all remember the Brandi Sisters." My heart started pounding a mile a minute and my stomach was tied up in knots and I knew the pill had worn off and that Mike had probably thrown the rest away, and I felt like there was no escape.

The emcee was saying, "Now we'd like to present the little one who was always in front. Remember her, the cute one with the bangs that you've seen so many times with her sisters? This is a great new venture for her, because she's coming out here on her own with a great voice and some great songs. So let's make her feel right at home. Let's welcome to the Saxony, Miss Nina Brandi!"

The band played my come-on and the audience did its duty with the hands and I walked out into the spotlight with a smile on my face and a bellyful of ice. I got through the first song to medium applause. The second song started me downhill. By the third song they were staring at me, so I came back at them with an old number of mine that I used to do with my sisters called "I'm Just a Little Girl from Little Rock." That got some applause because people in the audience remembered it and it burned down the old nostalgia for them. Then I did a new song called "Nobody Calls Me Sexy." Forget it. It bombed so bad it shook Cape Canaveral. And then I was off and I couldn't even go back for a bow. The audience didn't want any more of me.

I skipped my dressing room and went right upstairs, and when I walked into my room the phone was ringing. It was the owner of the hotel. He was coming up to talk to me. In he walked with Mike and he said, "Nina, I know it's pretty tough, but I've got to say something I'm sure you know already. You didn't exactly set the house on fire."

"I know," I said, "but this is only the first show."

"Yes, dear," he said. "But this is not a rehearsal hall. This is the Saxony in Miami Beach. First of all, cut out that second number—it stinks. And the fourth number is not strong, so that goes too!"

"That leaves me with three numbers!"

"Just do the three numbers, honey," Mike said. "Just get on and get off, all right?"

I nodded my head. What else could I do?

"Of course, now you can't close the show," the owner said. "You're not strong enough."

"All right," I said, still trying for a few points. "I'll follow the dancer."

"Forget it," he said. "He's too strong for you. You'll have to open."

"Open the show!" The floor fell out from under me. "You mean that's what I've become in one show, an opening act?"

"Either that," the man said, "or you can take the plane back," and he looked at Mike. "We'll have to cancel her out. Either or. Tell her to make up her mind." And he walked out.

Mike put an arm around my shoulder and said, "Look, Nina, we can't let them cancel you out, because all the offices in New York will know it. Everybody will know that you were a flop."

"But, Mike," I said, "what will they think when they hear that I went from last place to first place and from seven songs to three? Doesn't that answer the question?"

"I can always get out of it somehow." His practical mind was hard at work. "The timing was off. Or the arrangements were written wrong. Something was wrong, but not you. You've got to go along with this. You've got to save your face. And mine."

I gave up. I didn't have any of the old fighting Grandma left in me at that point.

"All right, Mike," I said. "I'll do it just for you. Thank God, it's only a six-day engagement."

"That's the spirit, honey," he said, squeezing my shoulder. "Listen, this is only the beginning of a lot of great things. You'll see, you'll do great. You just have to get used to being on your own."

Somehow I got through the second show that night. You can put a dress on a bear and have him growl for three numbers and he'll go over. Anyhow, nobody can tell whether you're going over or not when you open the show because by the time the end of the show comes around, they've forgotten all about you, and that's it, right?

When the last show was over, I went into the bar and sat down at one end by myself. I ordered my favorite drink for moments of crisis, a scotch, and tried to put myself in the frame of mind where I could get accustomed to the fact that I practically had to start all over from scratch. I wasn't doing too well getting myself to swallow this when someone said, "Can I buy you a drink?" I looked around and there was Mickey Faye, and into my mind flashed the words I had used to Mike on the plane flying down—the first guy in Miami who talks to me nicely. Why not Mickey Faye? I accepted his offer and he planted himself on the stool next to mine and said, "What's a beautiful girl like you doing sitting at a bar alone?"

I can pick up a line as well as anybody, so I said, "I prefer it this way. Actually there have been offers."

"I'm sure," he said and he swallowed a double scotch neat.

"Joe's Diner down by the beach," I said, "they want me there to bring on the jukebox."

I was starting to feel sorry for myself, but Mickey wouldn't play my game.

"Knock it off," he said. "Look, I saw you with your sisters and you were great. You really stood out. So don't let this get you down. You'll make it. You have to make it, because you're made for this business, believe me. And don't ever make the mistake of leaving it, either."

He sounded so sincere and he was making such an effort to get my chin back up that I tried to smile, and then I felt worse than ever and dropped a few tears quietly into my handkerchief while Mickey sat by me drinking until I blew my nose and came up for air. Then we started to talk and we traded stories and reminiscences, and he told me about his life and how he'd been brought up in the business, just like me, without a chance to be a normal kid and play with other kids, which he had resented all his life.

After about two hours of this, with the bartender constantly refilling his glass, because Mickey can belt down the liquor twenty to your one, he poured himself off the stool and said, "Come with me."

"Where are we going?" I asked.

"Up to my room. I want to show you something."

I said *uh-oh* to myself and I felt very sorry, because I was really digging Mickey but not that way.

"Now, come on, Mickey," I said gently. "You're too big to need anybody to tuck you into bed."

He looked at me for a minute and then he laughed.

"Nothing like that," he said. "You got me wrong. Nothing like that, believe me. I get enough in the dressing room. All kinds. Blondes. Brunettes. Big titties, small titties, all kinds. A lot of big-assed broads. No, honest, I want to show you something and it's not etchings. Come on, you'll see. Come up and meet the real Mickey Faye."

I went with him to his room, or to be more exact, his suite, which the management had given him with a fully stocked liquor cabinet. As soon as we got there he said, "Go look in the closet," and started to pour himself a drink. I opened the big double-door closet and I couldn't believe my eyes. It was filled with games and toys. There were roller skates and baseball bats and mitts and hockey sticks and paddleball sets and yo-yo's and hoops and pogo sticks and bows and arrows and little guns that shoot arrows with rubber tips at painted wild animals, and wind-up toys like cars and airplanes, and an electric train set that was all set up on a board. And up on the shelves were all the electric games you see in the stores at Christmastime, and toy sailing ships, and Parcheesi sets and checkers and Chinese checkers and Monopoly, all the board games you ever played when you were a kid. In one corner, there was even one of the old-fashioned gumball machines filled with gum.

"What are you, Santa Claus?" I asked him.

"I don't give them away," he said, coming over to the closet. "They're for me. I play with them."

I looked at him like I didn't believe him, but he was serious and for a minute I felt a little afraid. He must have guessed what I was thinking by my expression, because he smiled and shook his head and said, "It's not like that, honey. Let me tell you something and then maybe you'll understand. When I'm down in the mouth and not feeling too happy, or when I need some relaxation or whenever I get tired of those dumb broads who are always parading in and out of my dressing rooms, I come up here and I sit down and I play. And you know what?

110

It's great to be a kid! Believe me, it is. You know something? Kids don't know what they've got going for them, because it's the greatest, and the dumb little bastards don't appreciate it, you know that?"

"But Mickey," I said, figuring that he was just tight and maybe kidding me after all. "Most of these games you need partners to play. You know, other people."

"Nothing to it," he said. "I get a couple of bellboys to come up here when they're off duty. Slip them a couple of bucks." Then he thought of something and laughed. "The first time they thought I wanted—" and he looked at me and grinned. "Well, you can imagine what they thought I wanted."

He winked at me and took another drink.

"You should have seen their faces. I had two of them up here and they were looking cross-eyed at me and I was waving ten-dollar bills around in their faces. Then I opened this closet and you never saw two such surprised faces in your life. They were more surprised than you were. Now they come up here whenever they can. They don't even want to get paid anymore, they have so much fun. I'll show you."

He poked around in the bottom of the closet in a big cardboard box and came up with a set of jacks. Real jacks, not those cheap plastic ones like they make today but the heavy metal ones like I played with when I was a girl. And he brought out the little red rubber ball, too. Then he took down a big checker board and put it on the floor in the middle of the room and sat down next to it and shook the jacks around in his two hands.

"Come on, Nina," he said, and he spread the jacks out over the board and bounced the ball. "Come play jacks with me."

I felt a little silly at first sitting down with him on the floor to play jacks, but I thought I would humor him because he had been so nice to me; anyhow, he was tight and getting tighter and how long could he play, right? Would you believe we played jacks the rest of the night? Honest to God! I got so involved I just forgot about everything and we played until it got light outside. Of course, the way he kept putting away the scotch, Mickey wasn't too hard to beat, but we had a great time, because who cared about winning? It was just fun being a child again, sitting on the floor bouncing a little rubber ball, and the only important thing was to grab up as many jacks in your hand as you could. Finally, even the great Mickey

Faye had to give in. He had one last drink and then he sort of toppled over and went to sleep on the rug. I knew I would never be able to budge him, so I called for a couple of bellboys and we got him onto the bed and I put a blanket over him and tiptoed out and went to my room to catch up on some sleep.

I didn't get too much of that, because about one in the afternoon the phone rang and it was Mickey.

"Hey, Nina," he said. "I got a great idea. Let's go roller skating this afternoon."

By this time I was feeling as if I didn't give a damn about anything, so I said, "Why not?" And that's what we did. He didn't have a pair of skates in his closet to fit me, so he took me to a sporting goods store and he bought me a pair of skates, the fancy kind with the boots attached, because they didn't have the kind that clamp. Mickey wanted to skate in the street but I wouldn't go for everybody in Miami watching two grownups skating around like a couple of ten-year-old's, so we went back to the hotel. First we tried the ballroom because it had a nice shiny floor, but the assistant manager came in and wouldn't let us because he said it would ruin the floor. Then we found the hallways in the service area around the laundry and the supply rooms where the floors didn't have carpets, and we had a ball. The cooks and the cleaning women and porters thought we were crazy, but we didn't care. We skated around them and between them and up and down the halls and through swinging doors into trunk storage rooms and linen rooms and towel rooms and a room where they stored bread, and we grabbed a long French bread off a shelf and ate it without stopping and it was one of the best afternoons I ever had in my life.

It was a great week, even with my flop. Every night I went on and did my three numbers, like Mike said, a fast on and off. And every day Mickey and I played with different toys and games. And one day we went to a little private beach that the hotel had reserved for VIP's and we threw a beach ball around and played quoits and built sand castles and sailed toy boats and made flowers and fruits out of wet sand, using those little tin forms they used to sell at Coney Island and Brighton Beach. The last day I was there I went to a toy store and bought Mickey a set of jazz drums, and he bought me a Mickey Mouse watch and a gold charm bracelet, with silver hammered into the gold by a special process, and all hung around with little gold toys. The next day, just before I left, I went up to his room to say good-bye. From out in the hall I could hear him beating away on the drums. We kissed each other and I left in a hurry so he couldn't see the tears in my eyes because I knew how lonely he really was. As I walked to the elevator, I could hear him playing a march on the snare to keep up my spirits, and believe me my spirits needed it because I was going back to New York a flop.

I had written to Billie telling her all about Brace and how I didn't feel I could go back to him, and she called me up and invited me to move back in with her, so for the time being, at least, I could look ahead that far.

Chapter
ELEVEN

One of the first things I did when I got back to New York was to break completely with Brace. I wasn't going to stick my head back in the lion's mouth by going back to him and risking another cut lip, or maybe worse. I called up the hotel to see if he was there; by luck, he was out of town and not expected back for a couple of days. They knew who I was at the desk; Brace had kept the wheels well-oiled so the management wouldn't make trouble for us, and the desk clerks didn't think anything of it when I walked in that same day, asked for the key, and went up to the apartment. I packed my things in a couple of valises, carried them down myself and out to the cab, and drove off before they knew what I was doing.

The second thing I did was to call up my mother to tell her that I was no longer living with Brace. She was very happy to hear that, though I didn't tell her why because I didn't want to hear any I-told-you-so's, not from her or anybody. She said the family split had lasted too long, anyhow, and she loved me no matter what I did, and I told her I loved her and I felt a lot better after that. Of course, there was no getting back with my sisters. Even if my pride would allow it, which it wouldn't, not after what we had said to each other, it wasn't possible because Marcie had dropped out of the act and two new girls had taken our places. From what I heard the act wasn't doing too well. The numbers they were singing didn't have the old zing and the bookings were falling off, and it was just a matter of time before the Brandi Sisters would be a thing of the past.

I went on trying to work up my own act and Mike Krantz kept trying to get me bookings—which wasn't too easy because in show business smash hits and flops make instant news. Every office from New York to L.A. knew what had happened to Nina Brandi in Miami.

If my professional career was at a standstill, at least my personal life had calmed down. Brace did not try to get in touch with me, and I had just about begun to feel that that episode in my life was over when the phone rang one evening and Joye Garrick was on the line. She came on all sweetness and light and sugar and spice and said she had been calling around trying to reach me and had finally called my mother for my number, and it was too bad about Miami but that I should keep plugging away because I was one of those persons who just couldn't miss, and so on and so forth. I waited for her to get to the real reason for the call, which I was sure was not to talk about me.

Sure enough, finally she said, "Nina, how about meeting me for lunch? I've got something I want to talk to you about."

"If it's about Brace," I told her, "I'd rather not."

"Oh, no! It's not about him, that bad boy. It's about my book. Remember we spoke about it? I think you might be able to help me, if you would. I want to get it just right because I want it to be very authentic. You know we plan to make a picture out of it, don't you? Well, there are going to be lots of parts in it for young actresses and performers. In fact, I'm sure you would fit one that I have in mind."

When I heard that, I picked up my ears because it's second nature for anybody in the business to line up work for the future. In fact, I just finished reading a book about Bert Lahr, and would you believe it, he was always worrying about jobs even after he was so successful. I said yes, I'd meet her, and we made a date to have lunch the next day in the Palm Court at the Plaza where she and Sam were staying.

I got there on time but she came in fifteen minutes later, which I realized right away was so she could make an entrance. She walked in from the lobby with two toy poodles on a double leash, one black and one white, and she was dressed in a white leather pants outfit with black

114

trimming that had everybody in the place looking at her. She handed the poodles over to the captain and after we had pecked the air next to each other's ears, we got down to business. She talked about the book and how hard it was to write about show business, which is what it was about, without making it sound corny and sordid, and we traded stories about the name people we knew. I seemed to know more name people than she did, and I did most of the talking while she listened and said things like "You're putting me on!" and "Is he really like that?" and "My God, who would have thought it of her!" and so on.

When we got to dessert and coffee, and this mostly one-sided conversation had died down a little, she looked up from stirring her spoon around in her cup and said out of a clear blue sky in a very quiet voice, "Did you hear about Brace? He tried to commit suicide last week."

That was a real shocker, and for a minute I just looked at her with my mouth open.

"He got his Reno decree, you know," she went on. "He was all set to marry you and then he came back from Reno and found you had moved out on him. So he took an overdose of sleeping pills."

So that's what this lunch is really about, I thought.

"That's just like him," I said. "He's just woman enough to do that."

"He's almost out of his mind," Joye said. "You should see him. He's lost about thirty pounds. He looks like hell."

"Is that what you really wanted to talk about?" I asked her sarcastically.

"Well, that and the book. I just thought we could kill two birds with one stone."

"If you're trying to get me to go back to him, forget it, Joye. I want no part of him."

"You know he got the Reno decree because of you."

"Yes, well, he was in the process of getting a divorce before I met him, so it wasn't because of me, Joye."

"No, but he lost a lot of money in the settlement because of the Reno decree, did you know that?"

"I left my twenty-thousand-dollar sable in his apartment. That makes us even."

She reached across the table and put her hand on mine and said, "Nina, the only reason I'm doing this is because I think a great deal of Brace. And I think a lot of you, too, you know that. After all, I was there in Las Vegas when this thing began between you and Brace, remember?

115

I thought it was good for both of you then, and I hate to see it break up now over a thing like this."

"How could it be good for me, Joye?" I said, trying to keep my voice down because raking the whole thing up all over again the way she was doing was upsetting me. "Because of him I had to have stitches in my lip. And maybe I bombed in Miami because of what he did to me, did you ever stop to think of that? And did he tell you about getting me pregnant?"

"That pregnancy was as much your fault as his, honey," she said. "And you can't go on holding a grudge against him just because he lost his temper once."

"Oh yes I can. There was once someone I really dug and I still torch for him and he hit me, too, and I've never seen him since."

"Yes, but this is different, isn't it, Nina? I had a long talk with Brace in the hospital last week and he told me about that bitch Selma calling you. That had a lot to do with it, didn't it?"

"That had everything to do with it."

"Do you believe what she told you?"

"That's what he asked me before the lights went out," I told her, being sarcastic again.

"Yes, but do you believe it?"

I didn't know how to answer.

"I don't know, Joye. He never showed it in front of me."

"There, you see!"

"Yes, but what did she have to gain by calling me and telling me that? After all, she's getting her settlement. She didn't have to come up with a story like that. She could have told me a million stories about the broads he slept with instead."

"Listen, Nina," Joye said, "I've known Brace for years and I've never heard anything like that about him."

"Maybe he's kept himself protected. After all, you don't know everything about his private life, do you?"

"I think I know him well enough to rule him out as a homosexual," she said, looking me straight in the eye.

I felt myself weakening a little.

"He was also pretty weird in bed," I said. "And strange, too."

"Did you enjoy it?" She looked at me and smiled with her eyebrows up.

"Well, yes, in a way. I have to admit I did. But that's not enough to send me back to him."

116

She put her lips together like she has a habit of doing and looked down at her hands which were playing around with a knife and fork and she said, "Well, I think you ought to tell him all this yourself right to his face."

"I don't want to see him again."

"I think it would be a way for you to make the break final. You see, he's very sorry for what he did and he's living on hope because he thinks that maybe after all you might relent and give him another chance."

"He's just kidding himself."

"Then tell him so, to his face. Because I'm worried about him, Nina. There are a lot of big things lined up for him in the future, but if he doesn't pull himself together, it's all going to go down the drain."

"Couldn't happen to a more deserving guy."

"It would make you look a lot better, too. You know, most people don't know all the facts. All they know is that you were living together and he spent a lot of money on you and then you walked out. To them it's like another Nina Brandi story in the columns, only this time somebody almost died."

I stared at her and thought maybe she was right. After all, one thing I did want to do was to straighten out that reputation I had for playing around, because otherwise I couldn't see how any man could ever take me seriously.

"All right," I said. "I'll see him. Tell him I'll meet him at the Colony on Thursday. Are you happy now?"

She gave me her sweetest smile and said, "Honey, you know what will make me happy? Seeing you two happy again, together or apart, I don't care how, but happy!"

Between the time I had this talk with Joye and the time I met Brace at the Colony, I swore to myself that I was not going to feel sorry for him, because that's my weak spot. If I see a stray dog in the street or a cat looking miserable and starving or some kid wandering around with no shoes, right away I want to pick it up and take it home and mother it to death. Then I walked into the Colony and saw that poor pathetic figure sitting alone at the bar having a drink and I knew I should have given up swearing. He must have lost about thirty or forty pounds, because he looked just God-awful, and if I had any doubts about what Joye had said about him, they all vanished on the spot.

He hugged me and I turned my face away so he couldn't kiss me and said very coldly, "The only reason I'm here is because of Joye."

"God bless you and thank you so much, Nina," he said, and he sounded as though he was dying to grovel at my feet and kiss my fanny.

"Let's sit down," I said, and we ordered drinks and started to talk. When I think back to that conversation I can see that while I kept trying to make it go my way, somehow it kept getting out of control. Not because he was so clever about it, because he wasn't, but somehow the situation got away from me and I still can't figure out why or how.

I told him in plain language, "I don't love you," and he told me, "I have so much love for you, it will be enough for both of us."

In how many Grade-B movies have you heard that line?

I asked him, "Don't you have any pride? I'm telling you that I do not love you," and he came back with, "I'll earn your love."

Another famous line, right?

"Everything you did was bad for me," I told him. "Breaking up my family; my abortion, my busted mouth. What else do you want from my life?"

And he said, "I want you, Nina."

"You can't have me. I'm not up for grabs."

"I'm driving out to Brooklyn tomorrow. I'm going to make it up with your mother. Believe me, I will, if it's the last thing I do."

"But what will that prove? You won't get to me that way, Brace."

"Give me a chance, Nina." Now he was pulling what he must have thought was the show-stopper. "You know, you and I have run around a lot in our time, but everybody has to settle down sooner or later."

"If they have something to settle down with," I told him, sure that was the last word. "But we really don't have a basis for marriage. I don't love you, Brace. Do you want to start a life with me and raise children on that?"

"I'll take my chances," he said, and I gave up. I finally got away from him by promising to meet him for dinner the following week.

During the next seven days there were flowers delivered to me with cards bearing sweet little nothings from guess who. There were also phone calls at least once a day, until I finally said to him, "Now, look, Brace, don't try to build this up and make a thing out of it. We're just having dinner, that's all."

But that wasn't all. By the time I met him for dinner at

Patsy's, he had been to Brooklyn not once but three times and, believe it or not, he had actually made up with my mother. To prove it, he had the waiter bring a phone to the table, and he called her right then and there. I spoke to her and she told me that she had him all wrong and that he was really such a wonderful guy. I couldn't believe my ears.

"How much did you give her to say that?" I asked him, not really meaning it, of course.

"It didn't make any real difference," he said, looking uncomfortable. "As a matter of fact, she was a little short because your sisters aren't bringing in the big bills anymore; so I gave her five hundred. But not to say that!"

I had only said it as a gag, but when I saw that I wasn't too far wrong I said, "What else did you tell her to say?"

"Not a thing, Nina, believe me!" and I believed him, because I knew that nobody could bribe my Mom where I was concerned.

"She feels the way I do," he said. "She'd like to see you stop running around and get married. In church."

"Not on a Reno decree, we can't," I said, without thinking. "We'd need at least a California decree for that!" Then I realized what I had said.

"But I don't have any intentions of getting married right now, and especially not to you!" I said in a hurry, but it was too late because his face was all lit up and he looked like he was ready to grab me and kiss me.

"I told you I was going to earn your love," he said.

After dinner we found that it was starting to rain outside, so we walked over to his hotel so he could get his umbrella. When we got inside the apartment, he started to crumble at the edges because he said, "Come over here," in that old tone of voice.

"Oh, no!" I said. "None of that! We came up here for the umbrella and now we're getting a cab and you're taking me home."

He got himself back under control pretty fast and said, "But why go home? It's after midnight and it's pouring outside. Listen."

I listened, and sure enough I could hear the rain hitting the window and when I looked out it was coming down in buckets.

"I'd still rather go back to my own place," I said.

"I promise I won't bother you. It'll be a real test, to show how honest I can be with you."

I was pretty tired anyhow and it was late and raining so

I stayed. We slept on opposite sides of the bed, believe it or not, and he kept his promise and stayed on his side. In the morning he made me breakfast and served it to me in bed and I left early.

We started seeing each other about once a week after that. Was I crazy? Maybe, but at the time I didn't think so. I was really beginning to believe that Brace had changed. Maybe it was because I wanted to believe it. I also had a lot of second thoughts about his wife. I did a little investigation of my own along those lines. Every time I met anybody who had spent a lot of time working clubs on the coast or making pictures, I would bring up Brace's name and watch to see how they reacted and what they had to say. No one seemed to have anything to contribute, at least not any knocks. Maybe it was because by then everybody knew that we were going together again and they didn't want to say anything, or maybe it was because there was nothing to say. Anyhow, I started to think that maybe his ex had just been trying to hurt me from jealousy or whatever and finally I decided that until I found out differently for myself, I was going to believe him.

There was also the way he was taking care of Mom. Every week he'd go out to Brooklyn and leave a couple of hundred dollars with her, sometimes more—whatever she needed for groceries and the bills. And every time he did, she'd call me up after he left and tell me how wonderful he was. What could I say? Don't let him in the house? Don't take the money? After all, did I have the money to give her instead?

Brace and I went out a lot with Joye and Sam with them acting as chaperones. They made sure that after every date I went back to Billie's and Brace went back to his own place, because that was the only way I would go out with him—just dating, no sex. Sam was very good, playing the heavy father; he would say, in his usual way, "All right now, Ace"—he called everybody Ace and used hip talk which was very popular then—"all right now, Ace," he used to say, "you can take her upstairs to the door, but when it closes make sure it closes between you, dig?" I really started to like them and feel very warm toward both of them, especially Joye, because even though she liked to play the Hollywood scene, I thought there was a lot of good, sincere stuff underneath. And they were so concerned not only about Brace but also about me because I was his "girl" and it was kind of nice to have somebody older than myself acting like that about me.

Brace decided that we needed a fresh start all around. I told him once that I could never live in the apartment in the hotel again because it had too many bad memories for me, so he went out and found a new apartment, a really gorgeous place on Central Park West with a beautiful terrace and a big living room. He put down a deposit and had a few pieces of furniture moved in.

"All we need is a bed to start with," he said, laughing and happy when he finally got me to come up to see the place. "We'll get the rest of the furniture later on. And by the way, tell Billie not to make any plans for next weekend."

"What's next weekend?" I asked him.

"That's when she's going to be your maid of honor!" he told me, and he picked me up and swung me around and hugged me until I thought I was coming apart at the joints.

Joye and Sam took care of everything. They called up the Shore Plaza in Atlantic City and made all the arrangements, and I said to myself, Well, maybe this is the way it's supposed to happen, but I didn't remember Brace asking me to marry him and I didn't remember saying I would. I really didn't have time to think because it was all happening so fast—maybe I didn't want to think. Maybe I just wanted to get right into it and go along. It all seemed so inevitable, like it was bound to happen and I couldn't stop it, love him or not, because no matter how I tried to get away from him, I always seemed to wind up in the same spot, back at the beginning.

We flew to Atlantic City on Friday night, Brace and I and Joye and Sam and Billie and her boyfriend who she'd been seeing a lot of for quite a few months, a singer named Tim Tracy whom we all knew and who was a really gorgeous guy.

There must have been a thousand people there for the wedding. The Garricks had invited just about everybody they knew and everybody Brace and· I knew, too. Now, that was a real tipoff, wouldn't you say, the fact that aside from my closest friend, Billie, I hadn't invited anybody? And neither had Brace? Anyhow, all these people were there at Joye and Sam's expense. My sisters were still mad at me so they weren't there and my mother wouldn't come because, as she explained to me the night before when we went to Brooklyn to see her, she felt it wasn't really a

121

marriage but that when the California decree came through and we were married again in church, which we planned to do, she would come then.

There were cocktail parties and champagne parties and a shower for me, would you believe it, and a bachelor party for Brace, and a pre-wedding dinner on Saturday night before the ceremony which was scheduled for Sunday morning. Everybody was having a hell of a time except the bride, who was moping around thinking about how her family wasn't there and about her past experiences with her husband-to-be and how, maybe, she was not exactly doing the right thing.

I had asked Mike Krantz to give me away, and during the dinner he came over to me and leaned down to whisper in my ear, "Do you really know what you're doing?"

"I don't know for sure, Mike," I told him. "But I'm glad you're here. I need you to give me strength to say those two big words."

"Don't worry, honey," he said. "I'll stand by you, no matter what."

Even when Brace rented the new apartment and our marriage plans became definite, I had insisted that we sleep apart until after the wedding because I felt that it would add a feeling of sacredness to the whole thing, at least for me, so the night before the wedding I slept in my own room with Billie to keep me company. We didn't get much sleep, because I couldn't, and we stayed up most of the night talking. Brace was sleeping in the room next door, which connected with mine by a door in between, because we were going to stay on after the wedding for a honeymoon and use the two rooms like a suite. The door was locked on my side.

The next morning, I was up and out of bed at eight o'clock and getting dressed because the ceremony was supposed to start at ten. I was wearing a beautiful white gown made out of white satin and chiffon that I had picked out at Henri Bendel's, and they had put people to work on it overtime to get it ready for me in time—did that cost a fortune! Well, there I was in my waist-cincher and bra and the crinoline underskirt and in a mood which wasn't much better than my mood the day before, because I still had my doubts about this wedding. Then I overheard voices talking next door where Tim was helping Brace with his tie and tux. Something got into my head.

"Let's listen to what they're saying," I said to Billie.

122

"Let's not," she said. "You might hear something you might not want to hear."

"Don't be silly," I said. "Look, I'm going to marry the guy in a couple of hours, so why shouldn't I get to know him a little better. Come on, let's listen."

She giggled. "All right, why not?"

We stood right at the door and we could hear everything that the boys were saying.

The first thing I heard was Brace's voice, and he was saying, "Well, here I go. I just got a fucking divorce and now I'm getting married again."

Billie looked at me and tried to pull me away.

"Don't listen to this, Nina," she said.

"Be quiet and don't be silly," I told her, and went on listening because the little bell was tingling in my head.

"What's the matter, Brace?" I heard Tim say. "You love her, don't you?" and Brace answered him, "Yeah, I guess so. What the hell! I can't seem to hold her any other way. All the dough and the presents don't seem to do it. She just won't stay put unless I marry her. And to tell you the truth, I need to get married like I need a third ass."

That was all I had to hear. The little bell in my head was making like a fire alarm. I had my excuse. I started to bang on the door and Brace called out, "Who is it?"

"It's me, dear," I said in a loud voice. "I just wanted to tell you not to bother getting dressed because the wedding is off."

There was silence for a minute on his side of the door and then I heard him walk to the door and the doorknob turned but it was still locked on my side.

"Nina, open the door!" he said.

"Billie, lock the other door," I told her, and then I yelled, "And don't ever try to see me either. The wedding is off. You might as well call the judge downstairs and tell him. And tell our good friends, Joye and Sam, who arranged all this, too. It's off!"

"Don't be silly," he yelled. "What's wrong with you?"

"What's wrong with me!" I yelled back. "I've been listening to you through this door for the last five minutes, that's what's wrong with me. And I also know what's wrong with you, too. Well, you can go fuck yourself. The wedding is off and that's that."

He started banging on the door and calling to me to open it and the phone started to ring, and then someone knocked on the door and it was Mike Krantz. He had been getting dressed down the hall when he heard Brace and me yelling at each other and he wanted to know what was going on.

I let him in and told him what had happened and he said, "But you've got a thousand guests down there waiting for you."

"Let them wait, Mike," I said. "I'm not getting married to any Jekyll and Hyde. I want no part of him."

Mike shook his head and said, "Nina, you better go down there and get married; otherwise an awful lot of tongues are going to wag."

"Now, listen, Mike," I said, and the old Sicilian blood was really starting to boil, "you once told me that I had to finish out an engagement, otherwise my flop would be known all over New York. Well I did, and they still heard about it. I'm not getting married just to stop some gossiping tongues. They're going to gossip whether I get married or not."

"You know the smart money down there is giving odds that you'll never go through with it."

"Well, the ones who gave the odds are winning their bets because I'm not getting married. I want no part of this prick. He's the worst phony I ever met in my life. And you better get out of here, too, Mike, because you're starting to upset me."

"Let me fix you a drink," he said, and he started to fool around with glasses and a bottle from a tray the management had put in the room. Then the phone started ringing again, and I picked it up and it was long distance. A man's voice came on and said, "Hello, Nina, this is Jerry Miller."

"Nina! Nina, what's wrong?" That was Joye outside the door trying to get in. "Please let me in, honey." I was too busy trying to believe my ears to pay any attention to her.

"Mike, Billie, please leave!" I begged them. "And don't let anybody in, please!"

They slipped out and there must have been two dozen people in the hall outside, all talking at once and asking, "What happened?" and "What's going on?" And next door Brace was still knocking and pleading with me to let him in. His voice sounded hoarse because he could have been crying, but the only voice I wanted to hear at that moment was Jerry's.

"Jerry, is that really you?" My heart was going like a trip-hammer and I felt all the old excitement down in my knees.

"Am I too late?"

"Too late for what?"

"I heard the other night that you're getting married today."

"You mean I was getting married today, Jerry," and I told him what had happened.

"Nina, I called you for only one reason. To tell you not to marry this guy. Remember I told you about Bob Ford? And I was right, wasn't I? By the way, you owe me a phone call for that!"

"Yes, Jerry, I do. I have to admit it."

"Well, you're going to owe me another one if you go through with this marriage, believe me. He's not the guy for you, Nina. You'll never be happy with him. I hear too many rumors about him out here."

"But I talked to a lot of people from the coast, Jerry, and no one told me anything like that!"

"Maybe you didn't talk to the right people. You should have talked to me."

"What kind of rumors, Jerry?"

"Never mind about that. Just take my word for it. Don't marry him."

"I'm not going to. I just canceled my wedding. Here, wait a second."

I put the phone down and picked up the gown with both hands and right in front of the phone I ripped the bodice apart.

"Did you hear that, Jerry?" I yelled into the phone. "That does it! I just ripped my wedding gown. Now I'll never get married."

"Nina, listen. I'm calling from Frisco. I'm working a club here, but next week I'll be in New York. Will you have lunch with me?"

"Sure, Jerry, why not?" I said and he said, "I'll be talking to you soon, Nina," and he hung up. I put down the phone, feeling all mixed up. It was all happening too fast and I felt like I was being torn apart, with Brace in the other room crying for me and Jerry in Frisco still torching for me—it was just too much.

Then I heard Billie at the door saying, "Nina! Nina, open up!"

I let her and Mike back in and with them came a very distinguished elderly gent with gray hair and spectacles.

"Wait a minute," I said, stopping him in the open door very conscious that out in the hall the noise had stopped

125

and there were a dozen pairs of eyes on me. "Who are you?"

The man said, very dignified, "I'm the judge who's going to marry you. May I come in?"

"Oh, my gosh," I said. "Of course. But don't let anyone else in," because I could see Sam Garrick behind him trying to slip in behind him, and he was saying, "Now listen, Ace—!"

The judge came in and sat down and for an hour and a half he talked to me. He told me about his own daughter who was frightened about getting married and about how her husband had said a lot of things that he didn't mean before the wedding and she had said that she didn't love him right up to the altar and how this frequently happens when people get married. He said that I shouldn't forget that my husband-to-be had just gone through a divorce and maybe he was nervous about getting into another marriage, and just because he had dropped a few indiscreet words probably in jest that I had heard by eavesdropping was no reason to crucify him.

I tried to get in a word or two edgewise but that old judge just went on and on and there was no stopping him until he finally ran out of gas.

Then I said, "Yes, what you say may be very true, your honor, but you don't know the whole story. There's a lot more to it than this, and I don't want any part of him."

Up to then he had sounded nice and friendly, like a father trying to explain the facts of life to his daughter. Now he suddenly got very cold and he stood up and said, "Maybe if you did get married and did something for once that was legal and holy in God's eyes, you might have a happier life."

That stopped me cold. I looked at him and I said, "Do you really think so?"

"Nina," he said. "He's next door right now crying like a baby. Why don't you try to find it in your heart to forgive him one more time? Then if he ever makes another mistake . . ." and he shrugged his shoulders.

"Won't it be a little too late by then?" I said, and the judge answered, "Whatever you do after that you will have a right to do."

I thought for a minute about all this with Mike and Billie and the judge watching me and I walked over to the door between the two rooms and I could hear Brace crying and Tim Tracy trying to get him to stop.

"OK, Judge," I said. "But I'm not exactly in any condi-

126

tion to get married right now, and neither is he, I guess. Give me a chance to rest a little while. It's almost two o'clock anyhow. How about three o'clock?"

The judge agreed and he shook my hand and kissed me on the forehead, and Billie wiped her eyes and kissed me and so did Mike and he went out with the judge to spread the glad tidings. They sent up a maid and she took a piece of white satin ribbon from one of my bouquets and sewed it on the dress so that it hid the rip and looked like part of the design. After I had the dress on, I looked at myself in the full-length mirror that the management had sent up and I thought again of my mother and my sisters not being there and I started to cry. I guess it was a release after the anger and frustration of the past three hours and also because of hearing from Jerry again and knowing that I would never meet him for lunch now, because when all was said and done, I might still love him but I could never depend on him.

Billie made me sit down and held me in her arms and said, "Nina, don't cry. Maybe you will be happy, after all. Don't be so cynical and think that everything is going to go wrong. It could go right, you know."

Then the phone rang and it was Sam telling me it was three o'clock on the button and I blew my nose in Billie's handkerchief. We went downstairs in the elevator and when I stepped out an organ played "Here Comes the Bride" and with Billie ahead of me I walked into the room where the ceremony was being held. It was decorated with banks and banks of flowers along the sides and there were poles on both sides of the aisle at every row of seats, wound around with garlands of artificial vines, and there were streamers of flowers overhead all leading to where the judge was standing. He was smiling encouragement at me and Mike was there waiting to give me away and I could see in his eyes how beautiful I looked. Sam and Joye were watching from the seats right behind Brace and Tim. Joye looked worn and tired but she smiled at me and so did Sam and he made the three-ring sign at me. Brace was standing without moving with his back to me looking right in front at some spot behind the judge. When I was about halfway down the aisle, he turned around at last and I could see how swollen his eyes were from crying and how his face was still tear-stained. I guess I didn't look much better, because I hadn't had time to wash my eyes and fix them before I came down, and on both sides the guests were buzzing like a bunch of bees. When I stood next to

Brace and felt Mike at my elbow, I faced the judge, thinking about my father. I didn't cry thinking about him, but he was in my mind all through the ceremony, about how he was the first man in my life and the only one in my mother's life, and I remembered Jerry and how he would always believe I stood him up, and then I looked at Brace and wondered to myself, What the hell am I doing here!

The final words were spoken and Brace and I kissed and the organ played Mendelssohn and we walked back up the aisle and into the banquet hall. The party was terrific. It went on for hours and hours with photographers taking pictures every second on the second and people crowding around us to congratulate us, and the women hugging me with tears in their eyes, and the men bending over to kiss me and look down my dress which was kind of décolleté. I got dead drunk for the first and last time in my life, which I guess I needed, but Brace didn't get tanked up too badly. When we finally went back up to our rooms, he had recovered enough to pick me up and carry me over the threshold. I laughed and giggled all the time, and when he undressed me I just lay there laughing away. I have a dim recollection of him trying to make love to me and not being able to because I was half out and he couldn't get me to move. The last thing I remember about that night was his face looking tired and disgusted. And then he looked down at me and started to laugh and I passed out while we were lying on the bed, laughing together like two naked hyenas.

Chapter
TWELVE

For four days after the wedding, we didn't leave our rooms at the Shore Plaza. It was like Brace had never made it in bed with me before, which isn't too hard to understand when you remember that he had just been through a regular drought for two or three months at least, because we hadn't had any sex since sometime before I went down to defeat in Florida. And of course the big emotional crisis during the wedding, when he didn't know if he was getting me or not, had only added to his frustrations, so he was really busting his buttons by the time the wedding was over.

I have to admit that during those four days he was a changed man. I also have to admit that we lived on practically nothing but champagne, so most of the time I was kind of stoned, but I could see that he was trying. He waited on me hand and foot. Nothing was too much for him to do, and I'm sure that if I had let him he would have wiped my ass for me. He tried in bed too. He made love to me in a normal way, and he did his best to make it beautiful, soft, tender love like you read about in books. Of course his usual trouble was there to haunt him, because he had to make a big effort not to come as soon as he got in, but all in all it wasn't a bad performance and I started to feel that with time and practice he might make the grade. I guess the way I had almost left him waiting at the altar must have done a lot of good, because he really went out of his way to make me happy and contented, and I was, for the first time in I don't know how long. I even felt pretty sure about the future because it was beginning to look as though I had a fighting chance for a normal life after all.

Those four days were such a ball that we couldn't bear to go back to New York right away, so we flew down to Miami and fooled around on the beaches there and hit all the night spots and had a great time. When we finally did get back to town, we moved into the new apartment and started to fill it up with furniture. Believe it or not, in spite of my crazy on again, off again wedding, this was a very happy time for me. Brace and I went shopping together in all the stores along Fifth Avenue and Sloane's and the little expensive stores on Third Avenue where they sell antique furniture, and it was fun shopping like that. We were just like any other young couple starting out in life together.

We saw a lot of the Garricks again. They had us over to dinner at the Persian Room the night after we got back, and we went out with them a few times a week at least and spent a lot of time talking with them about our future, or, to be exact, Brace's future. They were both sold on the idea of getting him into television as a producer, not just as a performer, and when Sam offered to give him a hand, Brace rented a one-room office and started looking for network contacts.

Our home life was too lovey-dovey to be believed. He used to call me seven or eight times a day from the office,

129

so help me, and I would make dinner for him every night, and every night he would be there at six o'clock sharp to eat it. Can you believe it? My mother couldn't get over it, either. She came to dinner about once a week and she would say, "I bet he doesn't make it tonight," but come six o'clock we'd hear his key in the lock and there he was kissing me hello in the kitchen and taking Mom around and kissing her on the cheek. That's the way it went for weeks, and the few times when he had to go out of town on business or on location, he always made sure he got back the next day because he said he couldn't bear to be away from me for more than one night.

After about six months his California decree came through and we were married all over again in church. I went to confession beforehand and confessed everything, and the father gave me a penance and absolution and then we were married in a beautiful ceremony. This time my mother was there and all my sisters, too, because we had made up by then. The act had folded. Angie and Marcie were just being housewives and Dolores was looking around for some kind of business she could go into. All the bad things of the past seemed to be behind us and we kissed and made up like good sisters, and that made us all very happy because we felt that we were a family again. Of course, Mom still had the house so things were a little sticky with her moneywise because there was no more act bringing in the big bills. Brace made up the difference. He had made some good network contacts through Sam and appeared in a couple of TV specials. He also had his regular club dates and an income coming in from his Hollywood properties, so he went on slipping Mom a couple of hundred a week at least, and if the house needed repairs or if she needed an appliance or something, he made sure that was taken care of, too.

Joye was a regular visitor at the apartment. She would come for lunch once or twice a week and we would spend most of the time talking about her book, which was well under way by then. She always had some kind of question to ask about some show business personality, usually someone I knew, or she would ask me about vaudeville or playing club dates because she had spent all of her professional career out in Hollywood and this was all new to her. She told me that Sam had told her that he expected to get Brace together with some very important agency people and we could expect big things to happen after that.

Everything was duck soup, right? Well, yes and no. Like everything else in life, there was a fly in the ointment, and as things developed, it got bigger and bigger. I guess you can see by now that Brace thought that I was the greatest thing going in skirts. No other woman was as beautiful as me as far as he was concerned, and he acted as though he could never get enough of me in or out of bed. Now, according to what I had always heard from my married friends, the longer you're married the more accustomed you get to your mate, and after a while the sex thing cools off so that you're not panting for it all the time. With Brace it worked just the opposite. As the married months went by, he got more and more possessive about me and he wanted more and more sex. He couldn't stand to see another man look at me, and if he thought I looked back, he would get moody and sore and pick a fight which always ended in bed. It was all silly and kind of stupid because I was very happy with the way things were going and I wasn't even thinking about other men, let alone looking at them. I guess because of my vanity I was really pleased over the way he carried on about me. No man had ever felt as intensely about me as Brace did, and I thought I really must be something that had never been on earth before to make a man go out of his mind like that.

That was the way Brace acted, like he was out of his skull with love. He used to go crazy over my body. I was a lot younger then and I hadn't had any kids yet, so my body was young and very beautiful. My skin has this tan quality all over that comes from my Italian blood, I guess, and he used to go wild over it.

"Oh, Nina! I love your body so much! That color! Gosh, Nina!" And he would kiss me all over and nip me with his lips until it hurt a little and then he would go down on me. Only he wouldn't just go down for the one time. He would go down for ten or twelve times, and he would keep score by counting my climaxes until I begged him to stop.

"Just one more time," he would say. "Once more and then I'll let you go."

Moses was what I called him to myself. That was my private name for him. Go down, Moses.

The longer we were married the more he wanted. He never seemed to be satisfied. If we were sitting in a restaurant, just the two of us, all of a sudden I would feel his hand under the table touching my crotch. When we went out dancing, we wouldn't be on the dance floor two

131

minutes before I could feel him pressing up against me and getting hard.

"I'm going to make you come fourteen times tonight," he would whisper in my ear, and then he couldn't wait to get me home and on the bed. I used to plead with him to stop because he would go on and on until I was sore down there, but when I would say something, questioning him about going down so much, he would say, "Honey, we're married now. Anything goes. That's what married life is all about." And when I would beg him to screw me the regular way because after a while the novelty wore off and I wasn't really being satisfied, he would say, "We don't need that to be happy. Don't you understand? I love every part of you. Give me every part of you and I'll never want to go anywhere else."

Or else he would say, "God, I love your body so much. Look at you. What a skin! Honey, I could eat off your body."

And on some nights he would be so worked up that he couldn't go to sleep unless he was holding on to some part of me. "Just let me have part of you in me," he would say, and he would take one of my fingers in his mouth and go to sleep that way.

He wanted me to go down on him, too, but I didn't have the stomach for it. I know girls who are very experienced sexwise and they tell me they can't do it and that it takes a long time to get used to. Of course I know that hookers do it, but they get paid for it, right? I never could. I tried because I wanted to please him, but I could never do it to satisfy him. He would make me stop and tell me how to do it right, and I would try again but it never satisfied him and I would get disgusted and quit, or he would get mad at me and make me quit. After the first three or four months of married life, I think that he did the straight sex act with me maybe four times for about every thousand times we had sex the other way. I think his trouble was that he was back where he was before the honeymoon. He just wasn't able to hold back once he got inside and I began to see that it upset him so much that I had to be satisfied the best I could with his kind of sex. I used to go to sleep with the outside parts of my vagina all sore and tender and the inside aching, and I usually felt like I wanted something more.

One night Brace got home for dinner all excited. Sam had taken him to lunch at the Lambs' Club and he had introduced him to someone named Gordon. The name rang no bells with me which didn't mean a thing because in those days I knew very little about agencies or television, but Brace was very happy about it. This Gordon had just been promoted to a key spot in the American Talent Agency. The way Brace explained it to me, all the programming on the networks was being supplied by the advertising agencies who were selling sponsors plus shows, and the American Talent Agency—he called it ATA—was supplying all the talent, including producers, directors, musicians, singers, actors, writers—the works! Brace called it packaging and ATA was the biggest packager of them all. And since they controlled so much talent which could make or break the shows, it made them very powerful with the networks. And now there was this Gordon sitting up there very close to the top in the agency. To hear Brace tell it, Gordon was like one step away from the top.

Anyhow, Brace had had lunch with the great man, and by the time it was over, they had worked out a deal for Brace to star in a summer replacement show. According to Sam, this Gordon, whose full name, by the way, was Charles Hamilton Gordon the Third, was a real comer, and if Brace played his cards right he could hitch his wagon to Gordon's star and go up to the top with him.

A week later, Brace signed a contract to appear in the show, and since he had a voice in picking his supporting talent, he signed me as a featured singer. After that the togetherness in the Fontaine family was stronger than ever. Every day we would leave the apartment together, go to rehearsal together, rehearse together all afternoon, and come home together. Then once a week we would perform together on the air, so all that summer we were together twenty-four hours a day.

The show gave me a start again in the business because people started to see me again, including agents, and Mike Krantz called me up and we began to work on my solo act again. At the end of the summer Gordon pulled some strings and got Brace a network contract. He had an office which he shared with some producer and he was on salary. He and this producer were working on a daytime quiz show, but I never could figure out exactly what he was supposed to be doing on this show. He came home every night looking very happy and he was always very up about his future and what was going to happen to him there, and he was always talking about Chuck Gordon, because by this time Brace was calling him Chuck, which was his nickname and was used only by the people who were close to him. Brace was very impressed with Chuck Gordon, and when he told me about the nickname bit, he acted like God had given him permission to call him Pop.

I had yet to meet this Gordon, but I started to hear a lot about him, not only from my admiring husband but from a lot of other people too. At that time he was still married to the former Mary Marsh, who had started as a weather girl on a New York local station and then had moved up to her own talk and interview show before she married Chuck. They had been married for about fifteen years, but even though they didn't live too far from us, we didn't see too much of them because, as I heard it, their marriage was in trouble and they weren't doing much entertaining or appearing together in public very often. The *Times* did one of its Man in the News profiles on Gordon, and according to that he came from a very well-off family in the Middle West, somewhere around Detroit or Chicago, I think, and he had been to an Ivy League college, like Harvard or Yale. After his two years in the army he had gone to work for ATA as an assistant agent, and then had started moving up the ladder and kept on going up and up and there didn't seem to be any way of stopping him.

Later on, after he and Mary broke up, he moved into a duplex penthouse in Star House over on the East Side, that big, glass, boxy-looking building which looks like someone moved the U.N. uptown. At that time it was really Star House because it was just crawling with all the big names in show business and politics and Wall Street. Once he moved into Star House, he lived like a hermit, and all kinds of stories started to go around about him, stories about parties and girls, and once some hooker was found all beat up in his car while it was parked in the building garage. She tried to pin it on him, but he denied it and the whole business disappeared with her and was forgotten pretty fast.

The first time I saw him was his picture in *TV Guide* in a big story on the agency, and I didn't care very much for what I saw. He looked very Harvard and aristocratic, I guess you would say, and I thought there was something funny about his mouth. It was very full, like a woman's, and the laugh lines at the corners were too deep.

Gordon and Brace really hit it off together. Brace talked about him all the time and about what was happening at all the networks, and it wasn't long before Brace was on a network payroll as a producer with a couple of music specials to produce. Then Gordon had to go to the coast for a big powwow with the film studios which were producing all the situation comedies and Westerns, and he invited Brace to go along with him. When Brace told me that bit of news, I thought he was going to take off right out the window he was so excited, because by this time the rumors were flying thick and fast. The agency was in big trouble with a couple of the networks because two or three of its shows had bombed with low ratings, and the talk was that the guy who was president then, Arthur Count, was on the way out and the logical guy to take his place was Gordon. Anyhow, Gordon thought that Brace should come along to this meeting so he could get the feel of what was going on with the shows coming up for the new season, because Gordon had big plans for him.

Brace was going to be gone for four or five days and it was going to be the first time that we would be separated for more than a day since we got married, so when Mike Krantz called and said he had a couple of one-night bookings for me in the Toledo and Chicago areas I accepted because it fitted right in with Brace's schedule. We said good-bye to each other at the airport, because we left on the same day, and when the week was over, Brace called me in Chicago and I met his plane at O'Hare during a stopover and we flew back to New York together. Gordon was on the plane with a lot of other agency and network people coming home after the big meeting, and Brace introduced me to him in the airport lounge.

I'll never forget that first meeting. Gordon was talking to some people and Brace brought me over and said, "Chuck, I'd like you to meet my beautiful, Italian, dago wife."

And this thin man, who was maybe just a little over medium height, turned to me, wearing the face I had seen in the newspaper, and looked at me and made a face and said, "Oh, no, Brace! She's too much woman for you. You'll never be able to handle her." Then he turned back to the people he was with and went right on talking. And then it was time to get on the plane and that was that. I didn't much care because after seeing the guy in person I liked him even less than before, but Brace didn't know where to look. He didn't dare look at me and he kept looking back to where Gordon was sitting, but the great man wasn't paying him any attention. Then some man came down the aisle from the restroom, and Brace forgot about Gordon and poked me and said, "That's Arthur Count, the president of the agency. Boy, is he on the hot seat!"

Arthur Count was a worried man who looked like he should have stayed an accountant, which was what he was when he started. When we got off the plane at Idlewild, a group of men who were waiting came over to him and spoke to him. We stopped to watch and Brace went over with the other network people to listen and I saw Count get pale and wipe his face with his handkerchief. Then he hurried away with two young men carrying attaché cases, and some people shook Gordon's hand and he turned and said something to Brace and laughed and walked away to his car. Brace came back to me and said that Count wasn't president of the agency anymore. The board of directors had voted him out while he was flying back to New York, and Gordon was definitely one of the people lined up for the job.

The next few days were nerve-wracking for me because everybody was waiting for the board to meet and vote for a new president, and Brace was so nervous and irritable that he snapped at me whenever we were together. Luckily I was out of the apartment, busy working on the act because it hadn't been too successful yet. I had gone over better this time than down in Miami. At least I was a lot more relaxed and confident while I was standing up there by myself, but the material was still weak and some of the songs needed work and I was talking to my arrangers and rehearsing with Gus John, my piano player. In the meantime, Brace was under orders from Gordon to make himself scarce around the agency, so he just sat at home waiting for the phone to ring.

I came home one night pretty late and he was in bed watching television.

"Where the hell have you been?" he growled at me.

I told him I had been rehearsing with Gus, and he said, "Yeah, I'll bet!"

"Don't be silly," I said. "You know the guy's a fag."

"Don't say that!" he yelled at me all of a sudden, losing his temper just like that.

"Well, you know it's true," I said, and it was: Everybody knew it because Gus didn't try to hide it, and he was very nice and didn't act like a queen, so who cared? He and I got along like ham and eggs.

Then Brace started to yell at me about my dog, Jackie, because she was lying all over the bed, and I lost my temper and yelled back. I was getting undressed and I had my blouse and skirt off and I was just stepping out of my half slip when all of a sudden he jumped up and grabbed the dog by the back of the neck and threw her out of the room, right through the air. Then he slammed the door shut and I saw that he was naked and he swung at me and knocked me backwards into the bed. I lay there staring up at him. I wasn't hurt bad but I was shocked for a minute and so was he because he just stood there staring down at me, frozen. Then a crazy look came on his face and it was like a spring snapped inside him because he jumped onto the bed on his knees and started ripping off the rest of my clothes. I tried to fight him off but he was too strong and quick for me, and when he had me naked he lay down on top of me and started kissing and biting me all over my neck and shoulders.

Then he grabbed my head in both his hands and sort of groaned and said, "Don't you understand I love you so much I could almost kill you!" And then he went on kissing my body, going lower and lower until finally I felt him go down on me. I had my eyes closed and I was crying and half in hysterics because I was frightened, but he kept at me until I finally calmed down and started to respond in spite of myself and he made me come three or four times. Then he got on top of me and went in and came right away like he always did, and I felt his body collapse and we lay piled up on the bed like that for a long time. Finally he got up and went to the bathroom and came back with a Librium for me and we both crawled into bed exhausted. Sometime during the night I got up to go to the john and it was then that I saw the dried blood on my shoulder where he had bitten me. I washed it off and saw that it wasn't much of a wound, so I went back to bed. The clock said five in the morning and I remembered that in a few days it would be a year since we were married and I thought to myself, Happy Anniversary, and went back to sleep.

The next day Brace got a call to go to the agency. When he got there he was shown right into the president's office and there was Gordon sitting behind the desk. The board had voted him in. Brace called to tell me the good news and that he would be home late. He didn't get in until after midnight, and then he told me to get out his valise and pack it because he had to go back out to the coast the next day. One of the networks wanted the fall lineup changed. He and Brace had to get the film companies to change their production schedules, and they would be gone for another four or five days at least, maybe longer.

I was very glad that the days of waiting were over and I was relieved because Gordon was finally the president of the agency. That was good for Brace, and I was also relieved that he was going away, because after that session the night before I felt that I could do with a rest from Brace and his brand of sex.

After he left that morning, I called Billie and asked her to stay with me until Brace came back. I hadn't seen her more than once or twice for lunch since the wedding. She had been away a lot, playing club dates, and I really wanted to catch up with her because in those days I always kept in touch with old friends. She came over that night, carrying her little overnight bag. We had a nice dinner, just the two of us, and we sat around reminiscing about the days when we had shared the apartment on Eighty-sixth Street and about the guys we had dated, and we had a lot of laughs out of all the memories. Then I remembered Tim Tracy, the guy she had brought to my wedding, and I asked her if she was still seeing him. She said she was and gave me a funny look and started talking about someone else. About five minutes later I told her all about Brace and how well he was doing, and I said that maybe Brace could do something for Timmy. Again I got another one of those strange looks and again she changed the subject. The little bell went *ting!* and I got suspicious, so I asked her, "What's the matter, Billie?"

"Nothing, Nina. Why?"

"Because you get the damndest look on your face every time we start talking about Tim Tracy. Is there anything wrong?"

She said no and she insisted that it was nothing, but by now I could see that she was hiding something, so I kept pressing her for it because I had an uncomfortable feeling that it had something to do with me. I have an almost sixth sense about things like that; my philosophy has always been that it's better to find out what the problem is right away in the beginning and nip it in the bud instead of letting it make bigger trouble later on.

Finally she said, "How's your marriage going, Nina?"

"Great," I said. "He's a changed man."

"Do you really love him?" she asked.

"To be honest, Billie, I think maybe I do." I didn't want

138

to go into the sex problem just then, though I had it in mind to discuss it with her eventually.

"You mean, after a year you're not sure?"

"Well, I'll tell you, Billie. He loves me very much and I have a lot of security with him. We have a lot of money, more than I can tell you, and it's always great to be rich, right? And he gives my mother money whenever she needs it, and sometimes my sisters, too, when they need a little extra"—which he had been doing lately—"so what can I say?"

"But do you love him desperately?" she wanted to know, looking like she was suffering all kinds of agony while she was asking the question.

"No, not desperately. I don't think I ever will. Billie, what's it all about? Has he been out with a blonde? Come on, tell me."

"Nina, you know that I'm not a troublemaker."

"Honey, you're my oldest and best friend. Now, what's up?"

"Well . . ." and she took a deep breath. "A couple of months back Timothy was singing at this club in Brooklyn and Brace came in one night to catch his act."

"So what? I let him go out once in a while with the boys."

"Yes, well he must have been out with the boys that night, all right," Billie said, not looking at me, and the way she said boys it sounded kind of strange. "Anyhow they went to this club and later on when I met Timothy after the show . . ." She stopped and looked at me, and all of a sudden I knew that there was no blonde and it wasn't anything to joke about.

"Tell me the rest, Billie," I said. There was a funny feeling in my stomach that I knew what was coming.

"Tim said that after he was done singing, Brace asked him over to his table for a drink. And he said that all the time he was sitting there, Brace kept trying to rub his knees with his hands under the table."

"Go on," I said.

"Tim said that ever since the wedding Brace had been after him. He said it started during one of those parties at the Shore Plaza, only he didn't want to say anything at the time because things were bad enough as it was. And that night in the club Brace was after him for his address and his phone number. And just the other night Brace called him and wanted to know whether he was going to be out

139

in California where he could see him when his wife wasn't around."

"Are you sure Timmy isn't putting you on?" I tried to keep my voice steady because I didn't know whether to be angry at her or believe her. "I mean, is Timmy-boy all there? Does he have his marbles, like they say?"

"He's all there, Nina," she said. "I can vouch for that."

Then I told her about Selma's phone call and how Brace had acted and how I had decided to give Brace the benefit of the doubt.

She said, "Well, look, maybe you've got a point. I mean I didn't hear this phone conversation between Brace and Timmy, so maybe he is putting me on, though I don't know why he should. After all, he wasn't the first one to come up with a story like that. Why don't you play it smart? Keep quiet about it and don't mention it to Brace, because God knows what he might do to you. Just keep your eyes and ears open and see if you can't find out for yourself one way or the other."

I mixed us a couple of drinks and turned on the "Late Show" and we sat there watching the one-eyed monster for a while, only I was watching but not seeing because I was trying to put two and two together and get something. I thought about the phone call from Selma, and about his chorus broad in Las Vegas who was bisexual, and how all he wanted to do in bed was go down on me and have me go down on him. I didn't know too much about homosexuals at the time but I had heard enough bits and pieces to know that going down on each other was what they did. And I knew that he couldn't satisfy me the way other men could and that he was getting more perverted and violent all the time. Then I remembered what the judge had said to me before the wedding, and I wished I hadn't listened to the old fool.

Chapter
THIRTEEN

I had five days to sit around and think before Brace came back. I hated to think that maybe my marriage was a mistake. It was all I had, unless I wanted to get a separation or a divorce and go back to the kind of promiscuous life I had been leading before, and I knew damn well I didn't want that. The more I thought about it, the more I wanted to make the marriage work. Maybe sex with Brace was no bed of roses, but at least I had security and he was practically supporting my mother, which was something I couldn't do because my act wasn't making it yet.

Then I thought that if I could find out more about this homosexual bit, maybe I would know one way or another. I was afraid I would get my neck broken if I tried talking to Brace about it, but I thought that maybe if he was gay I could get him to go to a psychiatrist. Even if he had been to one already and it hadn't helped, maybe another one would. After all, I thought, aren't some doctors better than others? Why not headshrinkers?

I went to the Forty-second Street Library and looked up some books on the subject, but I didn't understand half the words so I couldn't follow what they were all about.

Then I tried talking to Joye about it without actually coming out and telling her why, but she only looked at me and said, "Are you still on that kick? Nina, there's nothing wrong with your husband, believe me. Why don't you just leave him alone and try to make the marriage work?"

Finally I had a brainstorm and decided that there was nothing like going to the horse's mouth. I had a rehearsal scheduled with Gus John before Brace was due to come home. When the session was over and Gus was putting away his music, I told him I had something I wanted to discuss with him and invited him out for a cup of coffee. He looked at me with a funny twist to his eyebrows and followed me into a Hamburger Heaven on Fifty-seventh Street and over to a table at the back where it was uncrowded.

Gus was a very sweet guy who had been around singers and music all his life. When he was young he had a drinking problem and it got really bad just as he was starting to make it as a songwriter. I heard that it was just because he was trying to go straight. He practically disappeared inside the bottle before he got hold of himself and went to A.A. to get himself dried out, and then to a headshrinker. By that time his songwriting career was on the rocks, and the doctor told him that if he really wanted to lick the bottle he should stop trying to be something he wasn't. So Gus gave up trying to go straight and started

141

living like what he really wanted to be, which was gay, and that cured him.

He went on making his living out of music, doing some arranging and working with singers like me and my sisters, which was when I first met him, because he was playing for us while the act was still alive. He must have been a very handsome guy when he was young because he was still good-looking, but in an older way. He always had a smile or a pleasant expression on his face, and he never lost his cool no matter what was going on around him. He never wore tight pants or the other gay-type clothes but he did swish a little when he walked and there was something in his voice, a sort of high sound to it that made people look at him twice.

I started out by talking about everything but what I really had on my mind, until he said, "Honey, are you having problems with your marriage?"

"Why do you ask that?" The way the question came out of left field threw me for a minute, so I stalled.

"Well, you've got something on your mind," he said, smiling at me and lighting a cigarette. "And for the past five minutes all you've done is talk in circles, so what else could it be?"

I beat around the bush a little more and then finally I got up the courage to ask the question that was bothering me.

"I don't know if he is or isn't," Gus said. "I haven't worked on the coast in years and he hasn't been in New York long enough to get a rep, so I don't know. Do you think he is?"

"I don't know," I said. "A couple of people have come to me with stories but that doesn't prove anything. And he is sort of weird in bed."

"That doesn't prove anything either," he said. "A lot of guys are weird in bed. Some people work out their problems in bed, you know what I mean? That doesn't make them gay. Of course, now, if you asked me about that boss of his, that would be a different story."

I couldn't believe my ears.

"You mean Chuck Gordon?"

"That's him. That's the one. Now him I know about. A real closet queen."

"But, Gus, he's married!"

"A lot of them are and some of them have kids. But you'd better believe it when I tell you that in some of the places I get to once in a while they call him Chuckee and

142

he wears a tiara, know what I mean? I'm talking about little places off Bleecker Street and in the East Village where a guy can walk on the street in drag and not get pulled in because the cop on the beat is getting copped himself."

"But he was just made the head of the agency!"

"Listen, you'd be surprised how many members of his sorority have good jobs with agencies and networks and other outfits, too." And he mentioned a national magazine and a film studio in Hollywood.

"But how can he get away with it? I mean, wouldn't it show?"

"Depends on how smart he is. Some queers never show it. Others make a big deal out of it. Some get in a tight squeeze and blow the whole thing. There's one thing about a queer like that, though. They like to have their own kind around. Watch and see what happens at the agency, especially at the top echelons. Pretty soon you're going to see the heads start to roll. Guys who have been there for years will walk into their office one morning and find the little pink slip on their desk. They're the straight ones, see? And then watch who he puts in their place. Before he's done, he'll have every queer in the business working for him."

By the time I was through talking to Gus, I knew a lot more about homosexuals than I had ever known, and he told me about some people I would never have suspected, but I still couldn't tell for sure about Brace. He did say one thing that made a big impression on me. Just before we said good-bye outside on the sidewalk, he leaned close to me and said in my ear, "Watch for the change."

"What change?" I asked him.

"In your sex life," he said, and he winked at me. "If it changes drastically all of a sudden, then you'll know for sure. That will be the giveaway."

Later on when I got back to the apartment, I found a telegram from Brace telling me that he was coming home the next day. He gave me his flight number but forgot to mention the airline, so I called his hotel to find out. The desk clerk came on and told me that there was no Brace Fontaine registered there, so I called his office at the network and his secretary gave me the information.

"By the way," I said to her before she could hang up, "I just called the Beverly Hills Hotel and they said he wasn't there. Do you know where he's staying?"

And she said, "Oh, didn't you know? He was there the

first night but he and Mr. Gordon checked out the next morning. He said there was some trouble with the rooms. Didn't he tell you?"

"No, he didn't," I said, trying to sound like it didn't matter.

"Well, I offered to call you myself," she said, "but Mr. Fontaine said he was calling you anyhow and he'd tell you." There was a question in her voice and I knew she was hoping I'd say something that she could dish out to her friends during their coffee break, so I said, "Well, he probably called but I was out at the time. Thanks a lot," and I hung up.

By the time Billie and I drove to the airport the next morning to meet Brace, I had a few things to think about. I wasn't exactly rushing off to see a lawyer just because my husband had switched hotels without telling me, but now on top of my doubts and suspicions about him I had the feeling that he could be hiding something from me and I wasn't exactly jumping for joy.

Brace came off the plane looking like Kid Hollywood himself with a straw golfing cap on his head à la Bing Crosby, a red turtleneck sweater under a white jacket, and navy blue slacks. He had the kind of body you see on male fashion models, with long, narrow shoulders that weren't too muscular so that they look lumpy and his torso narrowed down to a small waist, you know, the V-look, and his long legs ended in those slim, pointed Italian-style shoes he liked to wear. There wasn't a woman in the terminal who wasn't looking at him kissing me and wishing she were in my boots.

He handed me a long jewelry box, and when I took it I thought to myself that now I knew how every wife must feel when she's sure that her husband has been making it away from the home fires, and what had he done for me to deserve this.

I opened it and it was a watch crawling with diamonds and I said, "Darling, it's too beautiful. Thank you."

And he said, "Nothing but the best for you, sweetheart."

I waited for him to say something, like, did you try to get in touch with me at the Beverly Hills because I wasn't there after the first night, but he went right on telling me about the people he had met out in Hollywood and the shows that were coming up next fall and how smoggy L.A. was this time, and so on. And the more he talked, the more I got the feeling that he was trying to keep me from asking too many questions, because usually he doesn't discuss what goes on at the network with me.

Finally I decided it was time to stick a pin in him just to see how he would take it, so I said, "Oh, by the way, darling, I tried to reach you at the Beverly Hills but you weren't there."

"Oh, yes," he said, without changing his expression. "I was so busy I forgot to call and tell you. They didn't have room at the Beverly so I stayed at a place near the airport."

"That must have been noisy, wasn't it, darling?" I said, looking sideways at Billie, who was driving. She almost went into a car in the next lane.

"I didn't notice," he said, "I spent most of my time running around the studios and at night I was too tired to care."

Billie dropped us off in front of our building and when we got upstairs I braced myself for the usual bed routine, but he didn't seem to be in any hurry to get at me. Instead he took his time going over his mail and unpacking, and then all of a sudden he said like he had just remembered, "Oh, by the way, honey, I'm afraid I have some bad news for you. I can't have any sex for a while."

"What's wrong, darling?" I said, acting all concerned like the good little wife because by now I was convinced that something was up with him. "Are you sick or something?"

"Well, I went to my old doctor in L.A. for a checkup," he said, "and he said I should take it easy for a while. No sex, he said."

"Well, what's wrong? Did he say? Do you have a disease? Heart trouble or something?"

"Nothing like that," he said. "He's not sure just what it is but he took some blood samples, and until he gets the results I'm supposed to just relax as much as possible and not have any sexual relations."

Mamma mia, I thought to myself, he must have knocked himself out in Hollywood at those meetings. And then I remembered Gus John and what he had told me, and I realized what was happening. My sex life was going from weird to nothing. That's what I would call drastic, wouldn't you?

Brace had come back in time for our anniversary, which I was sure he had forgotten, but he didn't. In the morning there was a big bouquet of yellow roses, my favorite flowers, and that night we went out to dinner at

145

the Show Stoppers, which had just opened. Goldie Wolf, the owner, put us at one of the best tables, and Joye and Sam were there and a lot of people who had been guests at our wedding, and Billie showed up alone, without Tim Tracy, who was singing out of town, or so she said. Mike Krantz wasn't there because Brace didn't like him. There was a gift on my plate, and when I unwrapped it I found another jeweler's box inside and in it was an exquisite necklace made of diamonds and rubies and turquoises with earrings to match. It was from Brace, of course, only he wouldn't give it to me at home in private where he might have had to make a romantic situation out of it, right? Instead he did it in public in front of a lot of people.

Everybody oohed and aahed when Brace put the necklace on me, and Brace and I danced the first dance alone while everybody applauded, and they didn't know it but they were applauding his self-control because he didn't get a hard-on once while we were dancing.

Sometime later on that evening, Chuck Gordon and Mary looked in for a few minutes as every boss and his wife should, and he admired the necklace and danced one dance with me. While we were dancing, he looked down at the necklace and said, "I told Brace it would be terrific against that skin of yours."

"Oh?" I said to him. "Don't tell me you picked this out for Brace?"

"Let's just say I advised him," he said, looking me right in the eye. "I take a lot of interest in the people who work with me, Mrs. Fontaine." A little while after that he collected his wife and they said good night and left. I hadn't had much chance to talk to Mary on this occasion, which was the first time I had met her. She was an exquisite redhead with a figure like a high-fashion model and she wore clothes beautifully, but she seemed kind of nervous and like she was anxious to leave. At least she seemed relieved when they left, or I thought she did.

Sex wasn't the whole thing that changed during the second year of my married life. The whole marriage changed. For the next three weeks, Brace and I were very polite to each other, very loving on the outside, with lots of "Yes, dear," and "What did you say, sweetheart?" and "Of course, darling," passing back and forth between us, but aside from good-bye pecks in the morning and maybe another one at night, we didn't have much to do with each other. And there was no sex, right? But none. Doctor's orders, right?

He was very busy at the agency and that brought about a lot of changes, too. All of a sudden he wasn't producing just a couple of TV musicals. Overnight he was an executive producer and he had a producer working under him, and as the season went on his name as executive producer began to show up on the screen on more and more specials and all kinds of one-shots and he was busy running back and forth to the coast every other week. And every week there was another item in *Variety* about so and so who had been let go at the agency and about this or that person who was taking his place. The announcement always came from the office of the president of the agency and it was always a top job that was involved, so I figured that Gus John was right again.

At the end of three weeks of no sex he went down to Philadelphia to supervise some location taping and was gone for four days. The night he got back he was getting undressed when I noticed that his body was covered with what looked like welts and scratches.

"Good God, what happened to you?" I said.

"I think I've got an outbreak of hives," he said. "Must have been the sheets at the hotel."

Later on that got to be a favorite excuse of his, the sheets at the hotel. By this time the whole situation was getting on my nerves. I still hadn't been able to figure out the hotel-switch business in Hollywood, and the idea that I still didn't know for sure whether or not my husband was gay was annoying me too. I was in a really bitchy mood that night, so I decided to dig a little. Later on, digging into Brace would cost me, but I still didn't know for sure and I went right ahead.

"Looks more like somebody hit you with something," I said. "You didn't get beat up or anything, did you?"

"Where did you get that idea from!" he said, and I could see that he was getting irritated.

"Well, it doesn't look like hives," I told him.

"That's what it is. Now for Christ's sake will you stop bugging me about it!" And he turned off the light and got into bed and I thought to myself, What the hell have you been up to this time?

I lay awake thinking a long time after he went to sleep. I was really bugged by the way things were going. Even if his kind of sex wasn't exactly what I was accustomed to, at least it was better than nothing. Don't get me wrong. It wasn't that I was so hot for him. I still didn't really love him, not the way I had loved Jerry, but I was beginning to wonder about myself as a woman. Besides, I wasn't buying that phony story about the doctor and the blood tests, and while I had always known that there was more sex in our marriage than love, at least it made it a marriage. The way things were now, it was more like a marriage in name only, and who needed that? You see, I still had the old romantic dream in the back of my mind about settling down and having children, the whole bit. But how the hell could I have any kids if my husband was some kind of kook with wild, perverted sex one day and no sex at all the next? I had an idea that that wasn't the way husbands and wives stayed married or that babies were made, and I finally fell asleep deciding that I was going to find out about Brace once and for all, one way or the other. And I had a thought or two about how I could accomplish my mission.

I started by needling him about the blood tests.

"Gee, honey, it's funny you haven't heard from the doctor yet."

"Huh? What doctor?"

"You know, your doctor in L.A. Those blood tests he was doing on you."

"Oh, yeah. Well, I guess they ought to be coming in pretty soon. Any day now."

Then a day or two later: "Honey?"

"Hmmm?"

He was sitting up in bed, reading a script.

"Heard from the doctor yet?"

"What? Oh, no . . . no . . . not yet."

"Maybe you ought to call him?"

"Hmmm. What did you say?"

"There might be something wrong."

"Oh, yeah. Yeah. I'll call him tomorrow."

The next night during dinner: "Did you call the doctor today?"

"What? Oh . . . slipped my mind. I was busy."

"Why don't you have your secretary place the call for you if you're busy?"

"Yeah, all right. Tomorrow."

And so on and so on for a week. Finally, I guess he decided that he had stalled as long as he could.

Or maybe a little birdie whispered in his ear that he ought to lay the broad so she'd shut up, because one night he said, "Oh, by the way, darling, I finally talked to old Doc Adams. You know, in L.A.? There was some mixup in the lab and he just got the results back yesterday and they were OK. The tests came out negative."

I blushed a little or tried to look like I was blushing and said, "Let's go to bed early tonight, sweetheart. Is it a date?"

"Sure it's a date," he said, but for a guy who hadn't banged his wife in over a month he didn't sound exactly enthusiastic, and I don't think he was looking forward to eating snacks off my body, either.

It was his usual performance but minus going down. He got on me and in two minutes flat I heard the old familiar groan and he had shot his load. I wasn't anywhere near ready, of course, but I wasn't letting him off the hook that easy, because after he started making the moves I discovered that I really wanted to be laid, and by him, would you believe it? Maybe it was because I was still feeling bitchy and I could see that he really didn't want it. Or was it because I had the feeling that I was losing him and that hurt my vanity? After all, I was Nina Brandi, the glamorous, beautiful chick that no man could resist and every man wanted, the girl who could make a gorgeous guy like Brace go out of his skull. Only he wasn't exactly going out of his skull at the moment, so my ego as a woman didn't like that.

I held him in until I reached my climax, but when I tried to get him to do it again, he moved away from my hand and said, "Don't drain me!"

I said, "What?" because I didn't think I had caught the word right.

"I said, don't drain me," he said impatiently. "I've got a big day ahead of me tomorrow and I'll probably be home late and I need all my energy. Good night, honey." And he pecked me on the cheek and rolled over on his side.

That started me thinking and I wondered if I could put two and two together. For the past few days, Brace had been coming home every night at about seven, and usually when he did that I knew that he was in for the evening. If he had to work late he would either call me in the afternoon to tell me or he would dash home at five to change his shirt and say he had to go back to the office for a meeting or out to dinner with Gordon. I thought that maybe I could find some kind of pattern to the way he was acting that might tell me something.

The next day he worked late and the day after he came home, changed his shirt, and then he went out again, and it was the same the next day, too. I waited until the next

149

time he was home for dinner and the following morning, after he left for work, I called the agency and asked for Mr. Gordon. The switchboard connected me with his office and I spoke to his secretary.

"Mr. Gordon is out of town."

That was Miss Stephens, a real bitchy blonde who used to swing her tight ass and big tits at all the big shots. This is just the way she talked, too.

"Can I help yew?" with her voice up.

"No, it's personal. When will he be back?"

"Mr. Gordon will be out of town until Thursday mawning. Would you cayere to leave your nayem?"

I knew that she was dying to find out who this strange woman was who was calling her mysterious boss, but I said no thanks and hung up. That was Monday. Tuesday and Wednesday Brace was home at seven and in for the night. On Thursday he called to say that he had to have dinner with Gordon. At five he dashed in for a fast shower and a clean shirt and out the door he went in a big hurry. I said to myself, Aha, now I know. And then I thought, what did I know? That my husband had to work late when his boss wasn't out of town? So what? I was right back where I had started from.

Two weeks later Brace flew out to the coast again. Gordon had been there a couple of days already, and Brace came home one day at about noon and said that Chuck had called and told him to join him for a conference.

"By the way," he said to me while he was packing, "if anybody calls I'll be at the Sand Dunes. Anybody wants me, they can reach me there."

That night at about eleven o'clock I got a call from a writer who was working on one of Brace's shows. He said he had to speak to Brace right away because he just ran into a big bug in the script. I gave him the number of the Sand Dunes and he thanked me and hung up. Ten minutes later, he called again.

"I tried the Sand Dunes," he said, "but they say he's not there."

"I'll try for you," I told him. "Give me the number where you're at and I'll tell him to call you."

I took down the number and then I put in a call to the Sand Dunes. When I got the switchboard, I asked for Mr. Fontaine.

"I'm sorry, madam, but there is no Mr. Fontaine registered here."

"There has to be," I told her. "Look again, please."

After a minute, she said, "I'm sorry, madam, but his name does not appear on the guest list."

I asked for the desk, and when I got the clerk I told him I was trying to locate Mr. Brace Fontaine.

After a minute he said, "I'm sorry, madam, but Mr. Fontaine is not registered here." The little bell went *tingl* and I said, "This is Mrs. Fontaine."

"Oh, yes, Mrs. Fontaine. Well, you see he is here but he's in someone else's room."

"Really?" I said, and I knew that at last I was onto something. "Would you ring him for me, please?"

"Well, you see, Mrs. Fontaine, they left instructions that they were not to be disturbed."

"You mean they've gone to bed already? What time is it out there?"

"It's eight-fifteen, madam."

"That's pretty early to go to bed so I don't really think you'll be disturbing them," I said, feeling like I was about to swallow the canary. "Look, this is an emergency. You see, I'm pregnant and I must talk to my husband."

"Oh! Well, in that case . . ." and I heard him flash the switchboard and he said, "Put this call through to one-three-four-four please."

I heard the phone on the other end ring six or seven times and finally it was picked up and Brace said in a sleepy voice, "Yes?"

I said, "Brace!"

And he said, "Yes!" He was awake now. Wide awake.

"This is Nina," I said.

"What the hell do you want!" he snapped.

"I don't want anything, darling, but your writer is trying to reach you."

"I'm not supposed to be disturbed. Can't he wait until the morning?"

"He says it's an emergency," I said. "And I have some questions to ask you."

"Well hurry and ask them," he said, sounding like I was bugging him out of his mind.

"One, what are you doing sleeping at eight-thirty at night? And two, why are you sleeping in someone else's room? And three, who the hell do you have in there with you?"

Just then I heard an extension being picked up and a man's voice said, "Mrs. Fontaine, will you kindly not disturb us? If you ring this room again, you will not be put through." And both lines went click on the other end.

I was so mad, I lost my cool and rang the Sand Dunes again and got the desk clerk back.

"Please, Mrs. Fontaine," he said right away. "I could lose my job over this. They will not let me put you through to them."

"That's all right," I told him. "I wouldn't think of disturbing the lovers again."

And I slammed down the receiver. My little game was over and the final score was up on the board. I knew the answer to the question about my husband, that he was definitely gay, and I knew who belonged to the other voice, too. I had recognized it the minute it said Mrs. Fontaine, and it didn't surprise me at all. It belonged to the queen of queens, Chuckee-boy himself.

Chapter
FOURTEEN

Mom came to stay with me as soon as I called because I guess she could tell by my voice that something was wrong. I wanted her around because I knew damn well that as soon as Brace got home he would jump on me about phoning him at the Sand Dunes and I figured that he wouldn't start swinging if she was there. I hadn't told Mom everything, just enough so she knew that being married to Brace wasn't all bright lights and lollipops, like the song says.

Two days later Brace came home at two o'clock in the morning. Mom and I were fast asleep when I woke up, hearing the front door open and close. Then the ceiling light came on and he was in the room looking at us.

"I'm sorry, Mom," he said, "but you'll have to go home now."

"Brace, for God's sake, it's two in the morning. Let her wait until—"

"Here's thirty bucks for the cab." He pulled the bills out of his wallet and threw them on the bed.

"Now, Brace," my mother said in her sleepy, worried voice, "I hope there won't be any trouble between you and Nina."

"Don't you worry about that, Mom," he said. "Nina and I have some things to talk about which are strictly personal between man and wife. I'll get out and let you dress."

I put on a dressing gown and took Mom downstairs and the doorman got her a cab.

"Nina, please don't go back up there!" she said, hanging on to me. "I'm afraid for you."

"Mom, he's my husband," I told her, wishing to hell that he wasn't. "I'm sure he won't do anything to me, so don't worry."

"I don't like the way he looked," she said, and then she reached up and grabbed my head in her arms and looked up to the sky and said, "Holy Mary, mother of God, watch over my baby." And the cab pulled away and I went back up in the elevator.

Brace was in the bathroom when I got back, but as soon as he heard me he came out in his undershirt and jockey shorts. He was drying his face on a towel and he stood in the bathroom door, staring at me and not saying anything. He made me think of how he had acted the night Selma called because there was that same stillness about him, that same deadpan expression on his face. I decided that the best thing to do was to show him that I wasn't afraid of him.

"Why did you come home at this hour?" I asked him. "Couldn't you have gotten an early plane in the morning?"

"I couldn't wait to get back to my beautiful, loving wife," he said, and I thought to myself, Well, well, at least I've got him talking. I walked over to the window, which was on the other side of the bed, and I didn't want him to see how scared I was so I deliberately turned my back on him. That was a mistake, because when I turned around he was at the foot of the bed and I was cut off from the door.

"And I don't like the way you treated my mother," I told him, putting my chin up. "What's the idea of throwing her out in the middle of the night?"

"What's the idea of calling me up in the middle of the night?" he said, and he flicked the towel at me and caught me across the arm. It didn't hurt, it just sort of stung, but it was a kid's trick and it made me so mad I forgot that I was scared.

"Eight o'clock in the evening is not the middle of the

night," I said, and he flicked the towel at me again with a real vicious twist of his arm. I tried to grab it.

"Cut it out, Brace," I said.

"If I say it's the middle of the night, then that's what it is, the middle of the night," he said, raising his voice. "And I don't like nosy broads." This time he swatted the towel at my head. It didn't hurt but it upset me. It fell over my face and made me afraid all over again because I knew he could do a lot worse than hit me with a towel.

"You told me where you could be reached in case somebody called." I was trying hard to keep my voice steady. "Why did you shut the phone off?"

"That's none of your business," he yelled, and again he swatted at me with the towel. This time I grabbed it and tried to yank it out of his hands and we both held on to it for a minute, looking at each other.

"It's my business when you're in a hotel room in bed with another man," I told him, and then I was sorry I had said it. He gave a terrific yank and pulled the towel out of my hands. He threw it on the bed and walked toward me.

"Don't get me started, Nina," he said between his teeth as he came. "I'm warning you, don't get me started."

I could see that no matter what I said I was in for it anyhow, so I figured I would go for broke. Maybe I could get through to him and calm him down.

"Please, Brace, listen. We can work this out." I could hear how my voice was shaking but I went right ahead anyhow. "It's not so bad. If you went to see a psychiatrist, I'll bet that . . ."

"Goddamn you, you lousy bitch!" he screamed. "I am not a fag! Stop saying I'm a fag!"

"Brace, please, now listen—"

"I'm no goddamn fag, you cunt!" he screamed, and he slapped me across the mouth.

"Brace, don't hit me, please!"

He was on me now, slapping me across the face back and forth with his hand and screaming, "I'm not a fag, do you hear me? Stop saying I'm a fag! Lousy cunt!" Then the next thing I knew he had my pocketbook from off the dressing table and was swinging it at me. I'm one of those women who carry everything but the kitchen sink around with them. Well, that night the kitchen sink must have finally made it, because that's what it felt like when the pocketbook slammed into the side of my head.

"Ow! Stop, please!" I screamed, and wham! it slammed

154

into my head again. I slid down the wall to the floor holding my head in both hands, and I could hear the neighbors knocking on the walls and shouting that we should stop the noise. He kept swinging the pocketbook at me, but I had my hands raised so he was mostly hitting me on the arms. Then there was knocking at the front door and it was the doorman telling us that the other tenants were complaining. Brace got rid of him and came back and leaned against the bedroom door, looking at me. My head hurt like hell and I could feel that my ear was all swelled up. I looked up at him and saw him start toward me again, and I put my head down and covered it with my hands and arms. Then he was down on the floor next to me and he had my head in his arms and he was rocking me back and forth like I was a kid who had hurt herself and he was saying, "Don't make me do it, Nina. Don't make me do it. I love you so much, I could kill you, don't you understand? Don't make me, please!"

He lifted me onto the bed and started to make love to me. He took off my dressing gown and my pajamas and he kissed and bit me all over and hugged me in his arms and then he went down on me. I was half in hysterics by now, crying into my hands, and I couldn't catch my breath and stop sobbing and when I felt him down there I didn't want to see what he was doing so I put a pillow over my face to shut him out. But my head ached and my ear burned and hurt, and the feelings I had from what he was doing got all mixed up with the pain and he kept on until I was more hysterical. I took the pillow off my face and begged him to stop which he finally did and when he got up and looked at me he must have gotten frightened because he went and got me a Librium and made me take it and he put cold compresses on my ear until the swelling went down.

It took another Librium before I finally calmed down enough to get to sleep and when I woke up in the morning I still had the headache. I lay in bed all day trying to sleep, not even eating, while Brace tiptoed around and went in and out to the office and other places, I don't know where. I had to be careful about not lying on my ear because it was still sore. Once I woke up in the middle of the afternoon and Joye was there, sitting by the bed. She had a little notebook on her lap and she was busy writing in it, and when she saw I was awake she smiled and said, "How are you feeling, honey?"

I said, "Pretty good," and I wondered how much she knew about what had happened.

"My head still hurts a little," I said, and she said, "Well, what can you expect when you wander around at night and fall all over the place?"

She sounded like it was funny and she smiled at me and I thought, Boy, what a story he must have told you, but I was still too groggy to function, so I went back to sleep. Brace came back around dinnertime and he brought in some food from outside and made me eat it and then he gave me another Librium and a couple of aspirins which really knocked me out because I slept for the next twelve hours straight through. When I woke up the next morning the headache was gone and Brace was in bed with me, talking to his office on the phone. He was saying that he had a bad cold and he was going to stay home for a few days to take care of it, and while he was talking, he leaned over and kissed me.

For two days he kept me in bed, making love to me, and I thought that maybe after all he had worked the fagginess out of his system with Gordon, that's how naïve I was.

Being so violent with me must have made him focus in on me again, because as much as I could tell he didn't spend so much time with Gordon for the next couple of weeks. He was home every night for dinner and he didn't go out in the evenings. The few times he had to go out of town it was only for a day or two, and he always called me from wherever he was staying. It was like when we were first married, and this Jekyll and Hyde business had me so confused that I started to hope that maybe I could get him away from the fag bit altogether. I was also more than a little afraid of him. I never knew which way he would swing the next minute, to me or to Gordon, to love or to violence. And then there was Mom, the money he was giving her that she was living on and the wish I had to somehow make this marriage work, to make up for the way I had hurt her so she could be pleased with me and happy with the marriage.

He took off two weeks and we went down to Miami for a second honeymoon and had a great time. It was like he was a changed man again, like he had really gotten something out of his system. The only unpleasant thing that happened was the night we went to the opening of a new club called the Pirate's Cay, and who should walk in but Freddie Manners. Brace and I had run into him a couple of times since we were married, and each time he had given me the cold shoulder, looking over my head like I wasn't there and acting like I was a cushion he had to step over to get across the room. He really had never forgiven me for turning him down. What's that they say about a woman scorned? Listen, no woman has anything on Freddie Manners in that department.

Anyhow, we were with a whole party of show business people and the management was very happy to have us there for the opening because of the publicity, so all the tabs were being picked up for us and we were having a ball. Then I looked up and there came Freddie Manners with his usual wise-guy strut, surrounded by all his yes men and gofers. He walked up to our table, said hello to everybody, and then he spotted me.

Then he stepped back a few feet so he was practically in the middle of the floor and said in a loud voice, "The place is too fucking crowded for me!" and he started to leave.

"Don't go, Freddie," I said, and I got up. "I'm just about to leave myself."

"What's with you two?" Brace said. "Why the hell don't you kiss and make up already?"

"Is she really leaving?" Freddie said to one of his boys, and he looked around the room like he was patiently waiting but didn't have much patience left.

"Yeah, I'm leaving," I said. "I can't stand cheap joints," and I walked out with Brace after me.

When we got back to New York we got involved in a very active social life. Joye was finishing up her book and Sam had found a publisher for it and they told us that she was getting a five-figure advance which was close to six figures, and now that she was finished doing the hard work it was time to see New York a little. Joye had an idea that I had led such a busy life up to then that I didn't know my way around the spots. She was always saying, "Now let's see, where will we take Grandma tonight?" We got around to a lot of places but mostly we went to the Show Stoppers and sort of made it our hangout. Then Brace got too busy to go out most nights and slowly everything began all over again, the late evenings when Gordon was in town, the trips to the coast, the nights at home when Gordon was out of town, the whole bit. Our sex life went with all the rest until it was down to a quick bang once a week, like a train schedule, so help me. I guess it was supposed to keep me satisfied.

157

This time I knew who my competition was, so I tried to fight back, I really did. It wasn't even a question of saving the marriage anymore, it was my vanity more than anything else, or like the doctors say, my ego. I was really bugged about the whole thing because I felt that somehow I wasn't as much of a woman anymore. If the competition had been another woman, I wouldn't have felt so bad because another woman I could have handled. But a man! What kind of a triangle was that? How can a woman compete with a man for her husband's affections? How can she give him the same thing? Because at the time I thought that there had to be something special that Gordon gave Brace that I didn't have to give. You see how I was thinking? Like the whole thing was my fault. I never once thought it was Brace's fault because he was sick. I didn't start to think that way until later on when it was almost too late for me to save myself.

All through the second year of the marriage, I watched this thing between Brace and Gordon grow, and there wasn't a thing I could do about it. A thousand little things happened that wouldn't have meant a thing to anyone who didn't know what was going on, but I saw them and put them together and they told the story.

First, there was the look, that unmistakable look. The first time I saw it was in our apartment during one of the few times that the Gordons were there, and the talk was about a shakeup going on in one of the major studios on the coast. Maybe it was Warner's, I don't remember exactly.

Someone mentioned the name of the man who had just been made head of the studio, and Gordon said, "How's that for going up? Last year the guy was just another producer on the lot. Remember, Brace, we met Charlie just when he stepped on the escalator."

Brace said, "You mean when we tried to get them to speed up the shooting schedules?"

"No, not that time," Gordon said, and the way he kept at Brace about this thing I had the feeling that it was all for my benefit because he kept glancing at me to see if I was paying attention. "I'm talking about when you first met Charlie. The very first time."

"Oh, yeah!" Brace said, finally remembering. "That was the first time we went to the coast together."

"Right. That's the time," Gordon said, and they looked at each other like the memory had a special meaning for them. Believe me, I did not miss the message. It was like

158

the old they're-playing-our-song routine and the look went with it. It's hard to describe a thing like a look, but this one seemed to go right past the eyes and into where the special meaning was hidden. It was the kind of look you see pass between a man and woman in love when one of them comes into a room and they see each other for the first time that day. It's the look you see in the eyes of a happily married couple whenever their eyes meet by accident, the look that says, that's you, the person I love. As the months went by and I had many more chances to watch the two of them together, I saw that look pass between them time after time, and each time it seemed to be more intense.

I looked at Mary, who was sitting close by and listening, and she had a very strained look on her face. By this time I knew her a lot better because we had been going out in foursomes with the Gordons, and I liked her but I could see that she was under some kind of tension. The rumors about their marriage being on the rocks were all over the place. We got to be very close with the Gordons at this time, but it didn't last long enough for me to find out what the trouble was, though I of all people could guess. There was a kind of pact between the four of us. When Brace was out of town, the Gordons would take me out to dinner or send me gifts, and when Chuck was away we did the same for Mary. One night Brace and I took her out to dinner at the Forum, and while Brace was in the men's room, Mary started to question me about my marriage. She wanted to know how it was, were we happy, and so on. I was afraid to say very much to her because I was afraid it would get back to Brace and we'd have one of our fights and you know how those things always ended. Anyhow, while we were talking two fags swished by and I said, "Will you look at that! Isn't that gay?"

She looked at me and said, "I take it you're against homosexuals."

"Just the ones who hide behind their wives," I said, and we looked at each other and I think she was about to come out with it but just then Brace came back to the table and the moment passed. We never had another chance like that again, because soon after came Gordon's birthday party, which is another incident, and that was near the end for Chuck and Mary.

She invited us over to their place to celebrate, just the four of us. Gordon had very few friends. It was a very bad evening all around, very uncomfortable. It was supposed to be a cosy, comfy evening, but Mary was too nervous for that and very touchy. We were all sitting around in the living room, where they had what they called a conversation pit, you know, a sort of hole in the floor that you stepped into and there were cushions in it and a hi-fi set and a very low coffee table. It was big enough for at least eight people and we were sitting in it, listening to records, when Gordon came in from the bar with a round of drinks. He stepped down into the pit and squeezed in next to Brace.

"Charles, for God's sake," Mary said, and the way she said it she almost exploded. "Why do you have to squeeze in there? There's loads of room all over the place!" Chuck just looked at her and started to say something but he shut up instead and moved.

Later on we went into the den where Gordon's presents were and where Mary was serving us a midnight supper. As we left the living room, Brace and Gordon were having a drink and I looked back and saw Gordon raise his glass to toast Brace and he toasted right back. I stayed back to wait for Brace because Mary had gone into the kitchen with some dirty plates, and as Gordon followed Brace I heard him singing under his breath but loud enough so Brace could hear, "Beautiful, beautiful, black eyes." The real words to the song are "Beautiful, beautiful brown eyes," but, of course, Brace has black eyes.

Mary had Gordon's presents on display so we could admire them. Everybody who was in the business and his aunt had sent him something. There were a couple of attaché cases, very expensive ones with his name in silver or gold, and there were cigarette lighters, cases of vintage wine, at least two sets of golf clubs, and about six desk sets from Dunhill. Gordon had some kind of crack to make about each present and the person who had given it to him. We gave him a wristwatch; that is, Brace gave it to him because he picked it out. I had nothing to do with it but it came from both of us, right? It had a jeweled band and it cost a mint. I watched the way Chuck took it from Brace because by then I was watching everything that went on between those two, and when Chuck opened the box and saw what it was I thought he was going to grab Brace and kiss him right in front of me and Mary. Mary had waited to give Chuck his present and she brought it out now. It was a portrait of herself that she had had painted. I'm no big judge of art, but I thought it was just great. The guy who painted it had really got Mary into the picture. Looking at it, you almost expected the picture to move and speak. She had posed wearing an off the shoulders dress with a deep V in front and the shoulders and the top of her breasts looked like living flesh.

Later on, she told me that she was trying, through the picture, to reach Chuck just once more, sort of trying to give the marriage a last chance. Chuck hardly looked at it. He was paying more attention to Brace and the watch. Can you imagine? He just glanced at it, said, "Very nice. Thank you, dear," and went on talking to Brace about the watch.

I saw Mary's face turn white. Then she picked up the picture and walked over to Chuck, and when she was right in front of him, she said, "Happy Birthday, you bastard!" and she threw the portrait down on the floor in front of him and walked out. Chuck just looked sort of annoyed and went on talking, but I guess it was too much even for Brace because about fifteen minutes later he said, "Well, I guess we've got to be going," and we left.

Two weeks later I read that Mary had filed for divorce and it wasn't much after that before she had an Alabama decree. I heard that she was moving back to Los Angeles where she had come from originally, and when I called up to say good-bye, she said, "You know they're probably together right now, don't you? How do you feel about it?"

I didn't know what to say for a minute, and then she went on and I could hear that she was crying. "After fifteen years! Fifteen years! And that's the way it is, Nina. That's the way it is for me and for you, too!" And she hung up and that was the last time I talked to her.

Then there was what was going on at the networks, the way Brace kept getting all the choice shows to produce through ATA, and how he spent hours with Gordon over dinner or in the health club discussing the shows, and the ratings and time-rate cards as though he was Gordon's special and only adviser and nothing could be decided without him. In fact, I heard more and more about how if someone wanted to get a show on one of the networks, the guy to see was Brace. It didn't matter how big the party was, even the big star names, if there was something they wanted Chuck to do. Brace was the guy who could get to him, so step number one was getting to Brace, right?

"Brace has Charlie Gordon in his hip pocket!" That was

what you heard, and I was in a position to testify that it was true.

The health club belongs on this list. Gordon belonged to the Metropolitan Athletic Club, where he used to go to keep in shape, or so he said. Of course, Brace had to join, too. Anytime I wanted to find Brace and he wasn't having dinner with Chuck or in a conference with him or in some bar drinking with him, I'd know that they were at the health club. Not that they ever really exercised or anything like that. Brace wasn't the type and neither was Gordon. They never went in for anything more strenuous than a round of golf, at least not out of bed, and neither of them was a body-building nut, so that wasn't why they went there so much. The chief attraction at the health club as near as I could make out was the steam room. I think they spent more time together in the steam room than anywhere else, so help me! Anytime I called the club and tried to get Brace on the phone he was in the steam room with Gordon. They spent so much time in that fucking steam room, it's a wonder they didn't turn into a couple of clams. And if they weren't in the steam room then they were probably in one of the bedrooms that are reserved for members only, and the phone was always cut off so I couldn't get through.

And then there was the steak scene. It was performed one night at the Show Stoppers and the audience was a whole crowd of our friends. We were all having dinner together and the captain was taking orders. At the Show Stoppers the steaks are brought out on a big platter and each person selects one and then tells the captain what he wants on it and how to prepare it.

All the orders were taken except Gordon's, and when the captain asked him how he would like his steak, he said, "Brace knows the kind of steak I like. Brace, you fix it for me." So Brace had them bring out the olive oil and the oregano and the bread crumbs and pureed tomatoes and he made Gordon a steak pizziol just the way any wife would do for her husband, right? Not everyone noticed what was going on, but some people did and I saw them look at each other. Jerry Goldman, who used to produce television plays and still has his own talk show on the air, saw it all and he looked at me across the table like he couldn't believe it. I didn't know where to look. Believe me, it's quite a feeling when you're out with a crowd of friends and your husband is playing around with another man. Real fun and games, let me tell you.

162

Then there were the producers and actors and directors and musicians and composers and public relations men and chorus boys who got fired off network shows because Gordon was afraid that Brace was getting too interested in them. Or vice versa. For instance, there was James Riley, the star of "Foreign Affair," a very popular spy series. Of course it was in its fifth season at the time and it had lost some of its steam but not enough to cancel it. Anyhow, Jim Riley was a very handsome guy who, it seems, was one of Chuck's ex-boyfriends, pre-Brace, right? Well, everything was all right as long as Jim patrolled the Berlin Wall or chased young double agents on Sunset Boulevard after dark. But when he came to New York to lead the Macy Thanksgiving Day parade, and stayed around town and kept turning up in Gordon's office, that was a little too much. All of a sudden "Foreign Affair" developed bad rating problems and Jim had to drive his Alfa Romeo all around the shopping centers on a personal appearance tour which got him out of New York for the rest of the season. And when the fall lineup for the following season was announced, surprise, surprise! "Foreign Affair" was up in front of the firing squad. Believe me, I could make up a list of all these little things that were going on around the agency and around the networks that would be so long you would blow all your fuses. And through it all, the queen and his lover smiled right along having their affair, getting their kicks from each other like tomorrow would never come for them.

A lot of these things I heard about from very reliable sources or they happened where I could see them or else I would hear Brace talking to Gordon on the phone. They didn't have much effect on me because I really wasn't involved. I was too busy trying to keep up with what was going on in my bedroom, and that was something else again.

I said that my sex life had gone down again to practically the vanishing point once the great romance went into full gear again. Unfortunately it didn't stay that way which, believe me, I deeply regretted, because all of a sudden, Brace wasn't satisfied anymore with just going down on me. He came up with a whole new catalog of tricks, and he was always trying to turn the once-a-week bang into a two-person orgy.

One week he wanted me to tie him up in the bathtub with my nylons and hit him with his belt which, of course,

I refused to do. Another time he wanted to urinate on me, so help me! He was going down on me as usual, and I had just come up for air for about the fourth time when all of a sudden he let me go and stood up on the bed. I looked up to see what he was doing and there he was holding that thing of his in his hand. I saw that it was half soft and aimed at me, and I knew immediately what he was going to do.

I yelled, "Brace, don't!" and jumped off the bed in a big hurry. Do you know what he said? You wouldn't believe it any more than I did, and I was right there when he said it.

"Do it on me!"

I looked at him like he was crazy and said something sexy like, "What?"

"Please do it on me," he said. "Do whatever you want on me. All over me. Please!"

I told him that we had a bathroom for things like that and I wasn't about to turn my bedroom into one and to forget it. But the real shocker came when he wanted to screw me during my monthly. He begged me to let him at least four times that I can remember, and I think that shocked and horrified me more than anything else because it made me think back to the night of the abortion when I was still bleeding and I thought in my sleep that he was trying to get on top of me and pull out the packing. The whole scene came back to my mind and gave me nightmares all over again, and the worst one was that it was no dream and Brace was really doing it.

Why did I take all this shit? Why did I let him do all these things to me? Listen, let me tell you something, when you're in a situation like that there is no question of letting or not letting. You go along because you haven't found the strength yet to get yourself out of it. It's like being hooked on drugs or being a whore. Until you find something inside you that is strong enough to make you stand up and say, "That's enough! No more!" there isn't much you can do. And the reason why you don't have the strength to say no right off the bat is because as a woman you're so goddamn brainwashed by men. It's always men, from our fathers right down to our sweethearts and husbands and the bosses we work for and the managers who get us our bookings. They are always telling us what to do and how to do it and we listen and go along with it. If there's one thing I will never understand it's why women take all that shit that men are always dishing out.

For instance, take all that fucking nonsense, and I do mean fucking, that you read in the so-called sex manuals. You know all that let's do it inside out routine and you do this to me and I'll do that to you and then you suck me here and I'll chew you there stuff. Hell, outside of dykes, women never think of those things, and the only reason dykes do it that way is because the poor things have no choice, right? I mean, that's what makes them dykes, right?

The point I'm trying to make is that it's always a man who dreams up these things. It's always some man who uses his oversexed imagination to think up the really sick things. And then he talks a woman into doing them with him because she's always been so damn brainwashed all her life, especially about sex, and she goes along with whatever Brother Prick says. The real truth is that the average woman doesn't need anything more than a good stiff one in the usual place to keep her happy. All those far-out, wild, weird and wonderful ideas for screwing and banging are thought up by men because they're the ones who need them. Sure, I know, they're always doing it for us. It's for you, baby, to give you an extra thrill or a bigger kick or a longer climax. Bullshit! They're all designed to give the man more bounce to the ounce.

Besides, did you ever see one of those sex manuals that they sell through the mails these days? The illustrated kind? I got a brochure for one in the mail recently with sample pictures from the book, and just enough text showing so you want to buy it and see it all. I said, What the hell, and I sent them the ten bucks which I could ill afford because I figured it would be good for a laugh. Did I say a laugh? That book was a regular Joe Miller super deluxe special edition. I never laughed so hard in my life, because it didn't take any Mr. Portnoy to see that you had to have a pretzel-shaped body to make some of those positions work. And guess who wrote the damn book? Right the first time. A man!

It took two straws to break the camel's back, two little incidents which maybe weren't so little after all, and they made me give up on Brace. The first one was when I finally went down on him for the full count. He'd always been after me to do it and I had given up on it once, remember I said that? Well, finally I thought that I'd give it one more try. If I could do it as good as or better than Gordon or whoever he was getting it from, maybe I could keep him home nights. I did it, and then I had to run to the bathroom and throw up, and I knew that I had lost that round on all points. Do you know what that bastard had the nerve to say to me when I came staggering back to bed?

"That wasn't any good! You don't know how. You'll never know how. I can get my joint copped anytime so don't waste my time anymore!"

The second straw had a name. Chuck Gordon, better known as Chuckee-boy. And of course it had to do with another of Brace's sick ideas. For a long time he had wanted to—I don't know how to say this. I hate to even think about it. Oh, well! I'm only talking to you, so why should I be ashamed? After all, you'll only repeat it back to me, right? Anyway, he wanted to bang me in the rear. Up the ass, to be exact! Can you believe it? It was a big passion of his, and he kept after me for months about it, but really months. Now, I knew that that was something that homos do to each other, besides going down, so I was against it because of that. And besides, me and my weak stomach, just the thought was enough to make me sick, so of course I refused. Finally he stopped pestering me about it and I thought he had finally given up and I forgot all about it.

One Sunday afternoon after he had kept me in bed all day fooling around with him, I was lying on my stomach dozing. It was a warm day in June and we didn't have any clothes on, which was the way we usually spent Sundays at home whether it was June or January. He was looking through the Sunday papers and after a while he got tired of that. He started by kissing my cheek and neck. Then he worked his way down along the back of my neck and between my shoulder blades taking his time about it. I was half asleep and it felt good, like someone scratching my back with a feather, so I didn't object. Then I felt his hand between my legs and his fingers in my vagina and I got a little excited even though I was still half asleep. When I felt him get on top of me without rolling me over I thought that he was going to come in from the back. That's not the greatest position in the world for a woman, but getting Brace inside me wasn't something that happened every day, right? I drew my legs up and spread them apart to encourage him. Then I felt that his aim wasn't too good because he seemed to be a little too high, and I was just about to tell him when I realized what he

166

was trying to do and I woke up. It was too late. He was in and going in deeper. I almost screamed the plaster off the walls before he got a hand over my mouth.

When I was a kid, I remember how my mother used to give me enemas if I was constipated. I remember the old-fashioned red bag that she used to hang up on the shower curtain rod in the bathroom with the long rubber tube that hung down from it with the little metal thing on it to make the water stop and the hard black nozzle that seemed to take forever to go in even with Vaseline on it. That's what this felt like, except that Brace's thing was a lot thicker and it didn't have any Vaseline on it so it hurt like hell. He kept moving it back and forth and at first I tried to bounce him off but that only seemed to make it better for him because he said, "Oh, Jesus! This is the greatest!" so I just lay there and suffered until he was finished.

When he finally got off me, I walked around painfully for a while, cursing him. I had to walk with my legs spread wide because it hurt so when I tried to bring them together. I didn't want to look at him because I was mad and disgusted with him and also because I was afraid that I would be sick if I saw how his thing looked after being in me up there. And when I could finally go to the bathroom and sit down on the john and put cold cream on it to help the soreness there was blood on my hand. That was the first and last time he did that, because I never made the mistake again of lying on my stomach when he was around.

About two days later we went out to dinner with Joye and Sam and Gordon and some broad he brought along. This was after his divorce. Chuck had a string of girls he used to date when he had to go out as a couple instead of a single. I understand he used to pay them for the evening, and later on I found out that their services didn't stop when he dropped them off at their apartments. They were paid for the rest of the evening by the cut and bruise, not by the hour. And there was the night when Brace got a call at three in the morning to come down to some precinct house to bail his buddy-boy out because there was a girl in the emergency ward in New York Hospital with lacerations and bruises and a broken arm.

Anyway, I was wearing a tight sheath that night, so every time I stood up or sat down I took it slow and easy so I didn't open a seam. We were eating at the Forum, and Chuck took a seat next to me and when he saw me being so careful about sitting down, he leaned over and said in a low voice, "Need a rubber cushion?"

I looked at him and he was looking at me and grinning from ear to ear and I said to myself, That sonofabitch, he knows! And I knew there was only one way he could know. I looked at that grinning face and I wondered how much else he knew. And like he was reading my thoughts, he formed a word with his lips without saying it out loud, and the word was "Everything!" I went all hot and cold and I felt such a feeling of shame and humiliation that I couldn't stand to be anywhere near him or near my fucking husband.

I said "Excuse me!" and I went to the powder room and I sat there and I thought about a lot of other times when Chuck had said things to me that I didn't quite get at the time but that I knew now must have been his way of letting me know that he knew what Brace was doing to me. I cried until Joye came and asked me what was the matter. I told her to tell Brace that I had a headache and I was going home and I left and went back to the apartment in a cab. When I got home I went straight to the bedroom and started getting undressed. While I was taking off my jewels I saw a little pocket phone directory that Brace always carried with him. He must have forgotten it because there it was on his night table and it gave me an idea. I looked up Al Popper's home number and called him. Al Popper was Brace's private attorney at the time. Brace kept him on a special retainer to handle certain private matters, like the real estate he was always buying and selling out on Long Island, and Al read his contracts and advised him and so on.

When I got Al on the phone, I told him that I would like to see him the next day.

"Sure, Nina, honey," he said. "Come in anytime. What's it all about?"

"I'd like to get a separation," I told him.

That stopped him cold because he took a minute to think, and then he said, "Does Brace know you're seeing me?"

"Not yet he doesn't," I said. "But he will by tomorrow."

"Well, you know I feel kind of funny about this," he said, "because I represent Brace and now I'll be representing you. I don't know if it's ethical for me to represent both of you at once."

"Well, all I want is a separation at this point, Al," I told him, "not a divorce."

"I'll tell you what," he said. "Why don't both of you come in tomorrow morning and we'll start working it out then, all right?"

Just then I heard the front door open so I said OK in a hurry and he said ten o'clock and then I hung up.

Brace came in and said, "Baby, what's the matter? Don't you feel well?"

"I feel lousy," I told him.

"Did you call the doctor? Is that who you were talking to?"

"I was talking to Al Popper," I said.

He looked at me and said, "Al Popper? Why? Are you in some kind of a jam?"

And I said, "I'll say I am. Namely, this marriage!"

I saw that deadpan expression come across his face, only I was too mad and hurt to be frightened.

"You're not starting that fag business again, are you?" he said, and I could tell by his voice that if I said the wrong thing he'd explode.

"I'm not starting anything, Brace," I told him. "It's just that this thing we've got here can't go on this way anymore."

"Why, what's wrong? Why don't you sit down here and tell me about it?" He sat down on the bed and motioned for me to sit next to him, but I kept away because I knew that if he got me on the bed he'd go right into a sex scene.

"Now, look, Brace," I said, trying to stay calm and cool. "I'm not asking for a divorce. All I want is a separation. Maybe for just a few months. So I can have a chance to think."

"What do you want to think about?"

"About us. About our marriage. And about our sex life. Because I've got the feeling that there's a third party in bed with us, you know what I mean?"

That was about as close as I could get myself to talk about him and Gordon. I didn't want to open that can of worms, not with just the two of us alone. That could wait until we were with Al Popper.

"Did you tell all this to Al?"

"No, I didn't tell Al anything. All I said was that I wanted a separation and he said for you and me to come to his office tomorrow at ten o'clock."

"You've been listening to a lot of stories and rumors, haven't you?"

"No, I haven't, Brace. I mean—it's got past the rumor stage. And I think it's time that we either start living together like two normal people or call it quits!"

Just then Jackie, my cocker spaniel, came out from under the bed where he liked to sleep. He wagged his tail and wiggled his fat little fanny and he ran over to Brace to be petted. Brace picked him up and cuddled him in his arms. Then he stood up with the dog and said, "You can leave right now if you like, but you'll have to leave without your pooch." And he walked into the living room. I felt a lump of ice form in my chest as I ran after him and I saw him go out onto the terrace with the dog.

"Brace, what are you going to do?" I said. He walked to the end of the terrace and then he held Jackie by one hand over the railing with the poor little thing's legs dangling over twenty stories of thin air and he said, "You tell me that you're going to sue for a divorce or a separation tomorrow and this dog takes the fast elevator down. All the way to the street."

"You're crazy!" I told him. "You're out of your mind. You've got to be!"

"You'd better give me an answer before I count to three," he said, "or Jackie's going to make a big splash all over Eighty-fourth Street."

Jackie squirmed a little and yelped because Brace's hand was squeezing him.

"Take it or leave it," he said.

I had no choice.

"You win, Brace," I said. "You win round one. Now give me back my dog."

Chapter

FIFTEEN

The phone woke me up out of a sound sleep. I switched on the bed lamp and it was four o'clock in the morning. Brace had taken himself to his health club for the night, so I thought to myself, I bet the sonofabitch has gotten himself tanked up and now he's going to beg for my forgiveness.

When I picked up the receiver, I found Al Popper on the other end.

"Look, Nina," he said, speaking very fast like he was nervous and in a hurry. "I'm afraid we'll have to call off our appointment."

"You didn't have to call me to tell me that, Al," I said. "Especially at four in the morning. I was going to call you later on and tell you the same thing."

"Just as well," he said, "because I can't handle your case."

"Al, what happened? Are you all right?"

"I'm fine," he said, "and I want to stay that way. Brace called me a few minutes ago, woke my wife and me up out of a sound sleep and told me that he would have a couple of hoods break my arms and legs if I even talked to you about a separation."

"What am I going to do, Al?" I said. "First he almost kills my little dog and now he's after you. How do I get away from this guy?"

Al took a deep breath and said, "Take down this number."

I found a pencil and took the number down and he said, "Now promise me you'll never tell Brace I did this for you."

I promised and he said, "That's the number for Steinhold, Farley, Bolster, and Schram. They specialize in cases of this kind. All the tough ones, the ones no one else will handle, even with crazy husbands like yours. Say that I sent you. If anybody can help you, they can."

After breakfast I called Steinhold, Farley, Bolster, and Schram and got an invitation to come in and talk. Later on that day, after rehearsing with Gus for a while, I took a cab to the Wall Street area and went up to the offices of Steinhold, etc., where I met Mr. Schram. Mr. Schram was a short, stout man of about forty and he talked like he was Little Atlas or the world's strongest small man.

"Mrs. Fontaine, I assure you that we have handled some of the toughest cases that ever went into a divorce court. We've had some clients up here who were in worse predicaments than yours and we got them away from their violent mates in spite of everything those poor, sick individuals could do."

Then he took down a statement from me and had it typed up while I waited so I could sign it. And then he introduced me to his law partners, all three of them, and they shook their heads and made little noises with their tongues when they heard the details of my case and said something had to be done and they would do it. And then I signed some more papers and started to leave.

"By the way, Mrs. Fontaine," Mr. Schram said while he was helping me on with my coat. "Where is your husband staying at the present time?"

"Well, as far as I know, he's at his health club."

"He has a key to your apartment, does he not?"

"Well he pays the rent, Mr. Schram."

"That's beside the point," he said. "This is your safety we're talking about. I strongly advise you to either have the lock on the front door changed or have a chain put on it. I don't think that you should allow your husband back into the apartment. You have every right after the way he has treated you."

When I got home I had a call from Brace and he wanted to know if I was still upset. I said that I was and that I didn't want to see him and he hung up without saying anything more. Then I called the super and asked him to change the lock, but he said that he couldn't do that without getting permission from the landlord who was down in Florida, out fishing on a yacht, and couldn't be reached. He suggested a chain, too, so I said to get me one and after dinner he came up with a twenty-pound chain and put it on.

I went to bed that night feeling very safe and secure because I figured that now that Brace was chained out, he could never get in unless I wanted him to. At about one in the morning I woke up and heard someone at the front door. I went into the living room to see who it was and there was Brace out in the hall with his key in the lock and the door open as far as the chain would let it go. He saw me through the opening and then he saw the chain and I saw him back away from the door and I thought, Thank God, he's giving up. And then he hit the door with his shoulder and the chain flew apart. I saw him coming at me with that deadpan look on his face and the lights went out all around me.

When I opened my eyes, there was a bright light shining right in them so I could hardly see at first. I tried to put one hand over my eyes to shut the light out but I didn't seem to be able to move it. Then I got the light into focus and I saw that it was the ceiling light in the bedroom. I was on my back on the bed and my chin hurt when I moved my jaw. I tried to move one hand to feel it and realized that something was holding it. I turned my head to look and I saw that both my hands were tied to the headboard with my nylon stockings. Then I tried to roll over to see better and I realized that I couldn't move my feet, either. I lifted my head enough to see that they were tied to the frame of the bed also with nylons and that I was nude. Then there was a sound and I looked up and saw Brace coming out of the bathroom. He was completely naked and he came over to the bed and stared down at me and I thought to myself, Jesus, help me, because I'm a goner now for sure.

I tried to say something to him but my jaw hurt when I moved it and all I could do was make a sound. When he heard it his face got very tense and he threw himself on me and began biting and clawing at me and pressing his face into my flesh and kissing me. He did the same old things all over again and he kept at me for hours, literally hours, because I looked at the clock on the night table a couple of times wondering when this was going to end and how much more time I had to live and I could see how the hours were going by.

After a while, my jaw didn't hurt so bad and I was able to talk and I tried to get him to stop, but he went right on doing his things, mostly with his mouth, and I could feel how every once in a while he would have a climax and then he would rest for a few minutes and start all over again. Finally about five o'clock in the morning, so help me, he got off me, all sweaty and covered with his own slime, and panting for breath a little.

"Please let me up, Brace," I said.

"Get yourself up," he said, and started to get dressed.

"How can I, all tied up like this?" I said. "Please untie me. A hand at least."

"You're so good at figuring things out," he said. "Figure yourself out of this one." And he finished dressing and left the apartment.

I started pulling at the stockings, trying to work loose, only I didn't seem to be getting anywhere. I thought about all the Western movies I had seen on television and how the hero was always being tied up and left in a tepee or a hut and how he always seemed to get himself loose, only he had a fire to hold the ropes against or a rock to rub against or maybe a beautiful Indian girl who took pity and cut him loose. Well, there wasn't a fire handy outside of the pilot light in the kitchen and no rocks on the bed and not an Indian in sight, so all I could do was squirm and struggle and pray that Brace wouldn't come back.

I guess Brace was never a Boy Scout because finally one

173

of the knots came loose and I got one hand out and then I untied my other hand and then my feet. When I got to the bathroom and looked at myself in the mirror I saw that my body was covered with bites and scratches and there were bruises on my thighs which he must have done to me while I was still out, and my legs and the hair between them were wet and slimy from him. I got into the shower and turned it on hot and full force and washed everything off me, and then I took a cold shower with the needle spray.

It wasn't until I stepped out of the shower that I saw his sign. It was lying on the lid to the throne, and it was written in red marker pencil on a cardboard he had gotten from one of his shirts just back from the laundry.

"You're doomed. You'll never get away from me," it said in big letters.

"Nina, this is it!" I said to myself out loud, and by this time, believe me, he actually had me talking to myself. "This is out of some Grade-B movie and it's got to stop because I don't know what he's liable to do next."

I called the police and told them that my husband had attacked me.

"Listen, lady," the desk sergeant told me. "You can join the club, if you like. Come on in and sign a complaint. We got a thousand of them here right now. We'll bring your husband in and put him in jail for the night. And tomorrow he'll get up in front of the judge in Domestic Court and the judge will tell him to stop being such a bad boy and that'll be it. You're much better off talking to your lawyer."

Later on I called Mr. Schram and told him what had happened and he said to come in and he'd make out another affidavit. I went to his office and the affidavit was typed up and I signed it and Mr. Schram said that now we had physical cruelty as well as mental cruelty as grounds and not to worry because he'd take care of everything! After I left Mr. Schram's office I walked around for a while, not wanting to go back to the apartment. I had a fear of seeing the broken chain hanging near the door and of going into the bedroom and lying down on the bed to go to sleep, the same bed on which just a few hours before I had been tied up, and frightened for my life. But there was no other place for me to go, because I didn't have the money, right? So I went back to the apartment and walked around it for about an hour, gritting my teeth until I finally calmed down and was used to it again.

Brace didn't show up that day but Joye came over for lunch. I hadn't thought about getting the super up to fix the chain and when she came in and saw it dangling with the screws yanked out of the walls she looked at me and said, "You look like you've got burglar problems."

"No, husband problems," I said, and I told her some of what was going on. I didn't describe all the things he had done, and I didn't tell her he had tied me up because I was too ashamed to go into details like that with her, but I told her enough and she looked astonished and horrified.

"I always knew he had a bad temper," she said, "but I never thought he would go this far. I'm going to have a talk with Brace. He always listens to me. What else has been going on between you two?"

I told her about Brace and Gordon and she said, "That's a pretty serious accusation to make about the head of a big agency."

"What's happening to me and my marriage is pretty serious, too," I told her.

"But you have no real proof," she said. "Any one of those things you told me could have a logical explanation, even the business about their being in the same hotel room together. Maybe they found that more convenient than having separate rooms. Lots of men on business trips bunk together because it's convenient. And it's a lot cheaper, too."

"On their expense accounts, they don't have to be cheap," I said, and she had to agree with me on that.

"But I hear very different things about Charlie Gordon," she said, and told me some of the things she had heard about how he and some of the top brass at ATA were always in his office fooling around with the secretaries and stenos and how everybody was talking about what a stud he was with women in that secret penthouse of his with the elevators working overtime to bring them up and down all night seven nights a week. Anyhow, that's the way she made it sound, so I said that didn't sound very normal to me and she had to agree again.

When she was leaving, she took me around and told me that if I ever needed help to call her and she would come right over and she would definitely talk to Brace and get him to control himself and she was a friend and would always stand by me no matter what.

Brace didn't come home for dinner so I put a small steak on the grill and made myself a salad and ate alone. At about seven o'clock the phone rang and it was Mr.

Schram. I could tell by his voice that something was wrong. He hemmed and hawed for a while, asking me how I was feeling and was I all right, and finally he said, "Mrs. Fontaine, I'm afraid I have some bad news for you."

I said to myself, here we go again, and I said to him, "Don't tell me, Mr. Schram, I'll tell you. You have a wife and children and you don't want to have your arms and legs broken."

He laughed a little, sort of heh-heh-like, and said, "You're a wonderful woman, Mrs. Fontaine, and it's a good thing you have a sense of humor because I'm afraid you're going to need it. No, it's not like that. No one has made any physical threats, but the pressure on us is terrific."

"I don't understand," I said. "What pressure?"

"It's coming from very high up. More I cannot say, Mrs. Fontaine, but somehow your husband found out that we are representing you and that you plan to bring action and someone is putting the screws on. I don't know just who is doing this, but I'm only the junior member of the firm and my partners are insisting that I drop your case."

"Please, Mr. Schram—" I started to say with my heart on the floor, but he said, "I'm sorry, Mrs. Fontaine, but I'm afraid there's nothing I can do." Then after a few more words of hope and encouragement, about how some other lawyer and so on and so forth, he hung up.

I walked around for the next two days talking to myself. And when I wasn't talking to myself, I was talking to Billie or Joye. I called Billie and told her what was going on and we talked for an hour on the phone and then made a date for lunch to talk some more. I spoke to Joye who came over for lunch one day.

I had hinted pretty broadly over the phone that things were going from bad to worse and the first words out of her mouth were, "What's going on now? Come on, let's have some girl talk." We sat and talked the rest of the afternoon and she asked a lot of questions and I told her a lot more, except for the intimate stuff about what had really gone on between Brace and me. I still couldn't talk to anybody about that and I can't even today, except to you, of course, but you're different. You keep what I tell you to yourself except when I flip the switch and then you play it back to me. Only to me.

I saw my arrangers once or twice and I had a meeting with Mike Krantz about some club dates he was trying to line up for me and I rehearsed with Gus John who looked at me with sympathy in his eyes when I flubbed and mumbled my way through the songs we worked on, and in between all that I had on my mind was Brace. He didn't show up once during that time. I suppose he was living at the health club or maybe staying at Gordon's place, because I was sure that that's who he was spending his time with but I didn't try to find out or get in touch with him. At least when I was in the apartment alone it was peaceful and quiet with just me and Jackie there, and I was beginning to think that I couldn't have cared less if he didn't come back. Of course the rent was coming due and though I could have raised some dough by hocking my jewels I knew that that wouldn't last long and that I couldn't go on living there indefinitely with the maid service and all.

On the fourth day Brace came waltzing in just as I was getting ready to go out to meet Billie for lunch.

"Hi," he said just as though nothing had happened.

I stared at him for a minute and then I went on putting on my hat and arranging things in my purse.

"Going out?" he said, sounding like Lord Tweedy Pants asking if tea was ready.

I didn't say a word. I just walked out. Billie showed up with company for lunch.

"Nina, this is Larry Fox," she said, introducing a very good-looking young guy. "Larry, meet Nina Fontaine."

Larry smiled and said, "I'm a fan, Nina. I've heard you sing. With and without your sisters."

"Thank you," I said "And where have I seen you before?" Because he did look familiar.

"I don't think you have," he said, "unless I've seen you in court. I'm a lawyer. By the way, you are happily married, aren't you?" The way he looked at me I knew that he was hoping I wasn't and not for business reasons, either.

"Larry handles a lot of separation and divorce cases," Billie said, with signals in her eyes and voice.

We had a very nice lunch and I decided that the reason Larry Fox looked familiar was because he looked like so many other young men around at that time. Same hairstyle, same clothes. In fact if I didn't know he was a lawyer, I would have thought he was with one of the big talent agencies. During dessert and coffee, Billie suddenly remembered an appointment with her hairdresser and took off, which gave me a chance to talk to Larry. I told him that I had a problem and that I was looking for a lawyer and he got very interested and invited me up to his office for a talk.

I spent most of the afternoon with him telling him about my problem and describing what had happened with the other lawyers. He was very sympathetic. He made me sit with him on the couch in his private office because he said that would be more relaxing for me, and at the end of the session he was promising to take my case and he had an arm around me and was comforting me and he said that I shouldn't worry about the fee because he would wait to be paid when the settlement came through. Sound familiar? It certainly did to me, but I needed him so I let him go that far, but I didn't encourage him to go any further because, to tell you the truth, there was something about him that I didn't quite like. I didn't know what it was but it was something. I am that way about people, and especially about men. The reason why I consider myself such an expert on men is because of the way they react to me. I'm a terrific sounding board for a man. I'm what most men want in a woman, or what they think they want, because I'm gutsy and earthy and sexy and I listen when they talk and I respond and I guess they think that I'm always promising something. Men open themselves up to me and it doesn't take long before they're telling me about their marriages and how disappointed they are with their wives who don't really dig them, you can imagine the whole bit. Anyhow, Larry opened up to me, enough so I could tell that he got a lot of fringe benefits out of his women clients and he was looking for some from me, too. But there was a minty expression in his eyes that I didn't like, so I held him off and left him making out an affidavit for me to sign.

Brace was still there when I got back to the apartment. In fact, he seemed to be there to stay just as if nothing had ever happened between us because he asked about dinner, and after dinner he watched some television and then settled down like he hadn't been away for three days. There was an armed truce between us and we lived together that way for a couple of weeks. He was very busy at the networks with all kinds of new shows but he was home every night for dinner and he stayed home in the evenings. I made a call to the agency, and sure enough, Chuck was away in Europe and not due back for some time. I saw Larry Fox several times and once I went down and signed some affidavits. Larry called me up a few times to discuss the case, and one day he said he was investigating Brace and getting ready to serve papers on him.

The day after Larry told me that, Brace called me up during the afternoon to say that he was having dinner out. He sounded very happy about something, and I figured that Gordon must have come back unexpectedly and the lovers were being reunited. I didn't feel like eating alone, so I called Billie. She came over and I had a barbecued chicken sent in, and we had a feast, just the two of us, with a bottle of wine. We were just finished eating when the phone rang and it was Brace. I could tell from the background noise that he was calling from a restaurant table.

"Hi, honey," he said. "I just wanted to talk to you."

"Really?" I said, very chilly and distant. "Why?"

"Because I was talking about you," he said. "I'm having dinner with a friend of yours."

"Listen, Brace," I told him, "anybody you're having dinner with is no friend of mine."

"Oh, you're wrong." he said. "You're dead wrong, Nina. This is a very good friend of yours. Wait a minute, I'll let you speak to the party in question."

He got off the line and I didn't hear anything for a minute because he probably had his hand over the mouthpiece. Then a man's voice came on and said in a kind of embarrassed way, "Hello, Nina."

I almost dropped out of the chair onto the floor.

"What are you doing having dinner with my husband?" I said.

"We just got together to talk things over," and then the phone must have been taken out of his hands and Brace came back on and said, "You know, Larry is quite a guy. We played golf this afternoon and tonight we're having dinner together. And in a little while we're due at—oh, by the way, Larry, what time is it?"

I heard Larry mumble something in the background and Brace said, "Larry's looking at the wristwatch I bought for him this evening. It's quite a watch, isn't it, Larry?"

I was too stunned to say anything, so he said, "Nina, are you there? You're not talking, honey. What's the matter?"

I said, "Brace, I think you are the lowest thing on earth. And as for that creep with you—!"

"Honey, don't take it that way," he said. "After all, Larry is one of the boys."

Billie stayed for the rest of the evening but we didn't know if Brace was coming back or not so she left at about eleven. I tried to sleep but I couldn't and I sat around feeling lower and lower, because everything seemed blocked all around me. And the longer I thought about my life and what it had become, the more I felt like I was in a tunnel without any light ahead. I don't know what time it was when I finally walked into the bathroom and opened the medicine cabinet. I took out the bottle of sleeping pills and I took a handful and swallowed them. I think I emptied the bottle. Then I went into the bedroom and lay down and after a while I stopped thinking because the noise in my ears was too much and I drifted off the bed and into the dark.

Chapter
SIXTEEN

I opened my eyes and there was a doctor standing over me holding something in his hands.

"How many did she take?" I heard him say, and then Brace's voice said, "The bottle's empty. She must have taken about fifteen."

He was a nice-looking young doctor and I thought he looked at me with a lot of sympathy instead of with that cold, fishy look doctors give when you're not a regular patient.

"She's coming out of it now," he said. "I'll pump her out and then you keep giving her milk. I think she'll be all right."

If I never have my stomach pumped again as long as I live I'll never miss it, believe me. When it was over and the doctor had left, I went back into a kind of stupor which I didn't come out of until late in the morning. I found Brace sitting by the bed and he told me that he had found me when he stopped by to pick up some shirts on his way to his health club. He wasn't being so aggressive with me anymore, and I could see from the way he looked at me that he was pretty subdued. I guess he was afraid that he had gone too far, and from the way he was talking, he was really afraid of what I might do.

"You know you could have died if it wasn't for me," he said, as if he was trying to make me see that I owed him my life.

"If it wasn't for you, I wouldn't be in this mess in the first place," I told him. "You and that queen of yours."

"What queen! What are you talking about?" he said, getting red in the face. "Now, don't start that again, Nina. That was Chuck's doctor who was here. Chuck called him up in the middle of the night and made him come rushing over."

You can just imagine how much better that made me feel, now that I knew that he had brought that closet queen into my private little mess. As if I didn't have enough Chuckee-boy in my life already. Brace went on talking about how wonderful Chuck had been and how much he was doing for us, but I wasn't listening. I was too busy trying to make up my mind if I was glad or sorry that I had been saved. At that moment with Brace in the room to remind me of what I had been brought back to, it wasn't even a tossup.

"Get out of here, Brace," I said. "Get out and leave me alone."

Then the doorbell rang and it was the doctor. Brace went away and the doctor felt my pulse and listened to my heart and took my blood pressure and said I was doing fine. His name was Alan Stone and he really was Chuck's doctor. In fact, his office was in Chuck's building. We compared a few notes and right away I could tell that he knew all about Chuckee-boy and that he wasn't too happy to have him as a patient. It was pretty obvious that he knew more about Chuck than he wanted to say. I guess it was professional ethics, right? But I got the feeling that he thought that something should be done about Chuck. Later on when we got to know each other better, Alan told me about Chuck's girls and how he had to patch them up after Chuck got through with them. He told me that he tried to get some of the girls to make complaints to the police, but Chuck always paid them enough to keep them quiet, even with their broken ribs and the cuts in their breasts and thighs.

Alan stayed longer than he really had to. While he was talking to me, I could tell that he was trying to put me into a better mood. I could also tell that he dug me, and after a while I began to dig him, too. He was very warm

181

and easygoing, but serious, too, and when he talked to me he didn't make me feel that he was high and mighty because he was a doctor and I was down there with all the other know-nothings. He made me promise that any time I felt really down again I should either call him and he would come right over or I should go straight to his office.

The apartment was Grand Central Station that day; the minute the doctor walked out, Joye came in. She had met Brace and he had told her just enough to send her running to see me. She stayed with me all the rest of the day and she slept there, too, that night. I told her what had happened and we had another long talk about Brace and me and Gordon. She said I had to find some way of building a wall between me and them if I wanted to stay inside my skull. She also told me that she had gone to Brace's office and had a talk with him about me, and it had ended with him taking her out to lunch. And the lunch had ended with Brace's offering to help Sam get a show on the air. By this time, I knew Joye well enough to know that she would do anything to help her Sam, and the way she described that lunch I could see how inside of an hour, Brace had changed in her eyes from monster to saint. Somehow the real reason for her visit to Brace was lost and I didn't have the heart to tell her that Brace was paying her to stay off his back. He did get Gordon to put Sam's show on the air, by the way, a late-night musical revue kind of thing but Sam had to pay them both a $25,000 kickback out of the weekly production budget which they split between them. How's that for doing a favor for a friend?

The next day I was feeling a lot better and more in the world, so Joye went home and I was sitting in the bedroom doing my nails when Brace came waltzing in with a big cardboard box.

He threw it on the bed and said, "Truce?"

I didn't say a word, but I could see that it was from Bergdorf Goodman. Then he opened it and took out a full-length mink coat and held it up for me to see. I stared at it and at him, and I thought to myself, The sonofabitch is still trying to buy me, and then he put the coat on the bed, reached into the box, took out a muff and threw that on the bed, looked at me again with a kind of silly smile on his face and walked out.

I looked at the muff and I couldn't resist. I put the coat on and picked up the muff and I put my hands in it. Then

182

I looked at myself in the mirror and closed my eyes and I was with my father singing for dollar bills. I was six again, and I was wearing a pink, pleated Shirley Temple dress that I was crazy about and a coat with a muff. They were made for me by neighbors because the Brandis couldn't have afforded anything like them, not in those days. Neighbors were always making things for me. Not for the other girls but for me. It was always for me because being the youngest I was the cutest. That's why, when my father put me into the act at five, he made me stand in front of the others, right in the middle, and they sort of stood around me.

The coat was made by Mrs. Lefferts who lived downstairs. Mrs. Lefferts was a great friend of my mother's. She was always up in our apartment when my father wasn't home, and once she made me come downstairs with her; she took my measurements and went to work on her Singer sewing machine, and when she was finished, there was the coat. It was made of maroon velvet and it had buttons all the way down the front and gray Persian lamb fur trimming around the collar. It came with a hood which was fitted very snug like a bonnet and that was also trimmed with fur all around. But what I really loved was the muff that went with the coat. It was all Persian lamb, the same color as the trimming, and I remember the very first time I tried on the coat and put my hands in the muff, it felt like being with my mother. I can't remember how many times I took that muff down off the shelf in the hall closet just to put my hands in it for a few minutes. I used to have to sneak it down when my mother was out shopping and my older sisters were busy and not noticing, because that coat and muff were only supposed to be worn to go to church in the winter and on special occasions. I would close my eyes with my hands in the muff and it was like I was holding on to Mom. With four kids to look out for and never enough food in the house or money for shoes and clothes, Mom didn't exactly have a lot of time to hug and kiss us, not even her baby, which was me, and I guess the muff kind of made up for it.

I stood in my fancy apartment on Eighty-fourth Street on Manhattan's East Side, a long way from Sixty-sixth Street in Bensonhurst, and I looked at myself wearing my mink coat with the mink muff, a woman who was so well off she could afford to swallow fifteen sleeping pills all at once, and I thought of how my father would take me around singing when business was bad. And then I was

183

back in 1650 Broadway, which at the time was filled with agents. We would go from office to office. Most of the agents knew my father, so they would let us in and I would stand in front of them wearing my Shirley Temple dress and the maroon coat and holding the muff and I would sing for them. I would sing "South of the Border" and "A-Tisket A-Tasket" and "Three Little Fishes," all the hit songs of the day. And when I was finished I would pass the muff around and the agents and the people with them would put money in it. Usually it was only a dollar but sometimes there was a five, and once or twice there was a ten, and the man wanted to hold me on his lap and said to my father that he could leave for a few minutes if he had business elsewhere, and Pop laughed and made a joke and pulled me out of the office.

We would do that all day, go from office to office like that, and sometimes the people I sang for would tell us to go to so-and-so's office on the next floor up because he would love to hear me sing, and so on, until it was late. When it began to get dark, we would ride back to Brooklyn on the subway. I would have my hands in the muff and my head on my father's lap, and I would sleep until we went over the bridge. Then I would wake up to look at the lights on the buildings in Manhattan and I would have such a feeling, a kind of sadness because of the evening, and a sweetness and a wanting to be where those lights were, the bright aprons strung around those marvelous tall buildings. And I was happy to be with my father because I was hardly ever alone with him and I had the muff, too, which was like my mother. Then the train would go back into the tunnel and I would put my head back down on Pop's lap and all the rest of the way home in my sleep I could feel his hand in his pocket where he kept the money. And his hand would be moving and I knew that he was counting the bills over and over again.

God, we were poor in those days! I said to myself with my eyes still closed. Then I opened them and saw myself in the mirror again and I said, out loud, "You goddamn whore!" And I started to take the coat off, but then I thought again and I said, "Take what you can get. You've got it coming."

And I made up my mind that I would let things ride the way they were until I could get away from Brace. I wouldn't go to any lawyers again, not yet. First I had to make myself independent so I didn't have to depend on him anymore. Running away wouldn't have helped. There was only one way I could make money and that was by singing; if I was going to do that, I had to keep my name and get all the publicity I could get and play a lot of clubs and TV and how could I do that and hide from Brace? Wherever I went he would find me and come after me and maybe kill me. Once I had enough money and Mom wasn't being supported by him either, then I could give a lawyer a retainer and get divorced. By now I didn't give a damn about making the marriage work for Mom's sake anymore. I mean it wasn't worth my life, was it? But I did have to figure out how she was going to live once Brace stopped giving her money and the answer seemed to be me.

In the meantime, I decided to take all I could get, all the furs and jewels and the going to theaters and night-clubs and the best restaurants as fast as they opened up and the weekends in Miami and the resorts, the whole beautiful life that the beautiful people live. I was going to live it up on Brace's money, and when I could, I would just walk out of his life for good, in my own way and in my own time.

And that's the way it went. For a while from the outside it looked like Brace and I were going along the way we always had, the handsome, good-looking show business couple living the beautiful life, but inside, behind the scenes, it was get what you can, baby, while the getting is good. I told him I wasn't satisfied with just maid service anymore, so we had a full-time sleep-in maid. I said the car was getting old and we needed two anyway, so we bought a convertible with a fancy horn for driving around town during the day and going away for week-ends, and a Cadillac four-door hardtop for going out in the evenings to Broadway openings and the clubs and for driving up to Goldie's Show Stoppers. I had charge accounts at all the best stores, not much cash, I want you to know, but lots of charge accounts. Any time I felt the need of a little human companionship while I was walking around town, all I had to do was go into the Tailored Woman or Saks Fifth or Bergdorf's and talk to the salesgirls and walk out with another late-model evening gown or another fifty-dollar pair of shoes or even another fur coat. We moved to a new apartment, a bigger place just a block down from where Chuck lived, which was very convenient for Brace, right? There was a special closet in my bedroom just for my furs because besides the five or six full-length fur coats I had, there were capes and walking coats and jackets and throws and wraps and every coat had a muff, but six muffs didn't add up to six mothers. All of them together were only good for one memory, because I could only get my hands into one at a time, but they helped, believe me they helped.

The only real contact I had with Brace was the once every two weeks regular Thursday night bang. I guess that was about as often as he could get it up for me because after all what I had to give couldn't hold a candle to what he got from Chuckee-boy, right? I didn't care one way or the other. I just let him do what he wanted and I would turn off the light and put a pillow over my face and make believe it was somebody else, some actor or personality I really dug or some guy I used to lay before I married the queer who was down there between my legs doing his thing. And I didn't forget the check he gave me each week to send to my mother. He never paid it to her directly anymore. He used to make a special trip out to Brooklyn to talk to her and eat a plate of her pasta and then he would leave the check on the kitchen table where she would find it after he left. Now he made a big thing out of handing it to me to pass on to Mom. It was a reminder that I didn't need, believe me.

He went back to the same old pattern with Gordon. When Chuck was out of town, Brace stayed at home. When Gordon came back, Brace worked late. If anything, it got worse, and when Gordon stayed out of town for anything over a few days, Brace would get moody and irritable and he would snap my head off when I tried to talk to him. And I would try to talk to him, would you believe it? Because as the time passed and we went on with this game we were playing, I started to act again like the suspicious, jealous wife. I couldn't help it. I guess it was my vanity, because I still couldn't accept the fact that I couldn't hang on to a man because of another man.

Let's take a typical incident—Brace calls from the office and says he has to work late. That's at five in the afternoon. At one the next morning he calls again. I haven't heard from him in between, not even a message from his secretary. He's over at Chuck's and they just finished working, and he's on his way home. At three o'clock he finally walks in. It took him one hour and a half to walk one block. How's that for speed, Gonzales?

In the meantime I have had dinner, watched some television, walked the dog, and gone to bed. When he comes in, I switch on the light, look at the clock and say, "Where the hell have you been?"

"We've got pressures," he tells me. "So-and-so at this or that network is giving us problems."

I make him explain, and by the time he goes to bed, he feels guilty and I feel that I caught him at it again.

Why did I go through this kind of an act? Was it because pretending to have a marriage made me want one and I was mad at Brace for not giving it to me? Or was it just my vanity bugging me? I used to tear into him if we went out with Gordon and something happened like the steak scene at Goldie's, because incidents like that were always going on if Gordon was around.

"Do me a favor," I used to tell him when we got home. "Don't embarrass me like that again when we're in public, will you please? It's bad enough that I can't stand the guy and I have to go out with him. At least act like a man when I'm around. Don't make me look like the husband!"

"That guy you can't stand is putting minks on your back!" he would say.

"He put a monkey on my back," I would yell, "and you want me to kiss his ass for it?"

That was a bad one. That was one of the times when I would feel that I didn't give a damn and I would cut loose and we would have a fight. If I was lucky, he ran out to a bar. If I wasn't, he would knock me around, not too hard because he didn't want me reaching for the sleeping pills again, but enough to hurt me and send me to bed crying.

I just couldn't stop being a woman, whether I loved the guy or not, whether the marriage was good or not. I couldn't stop being a woman, and after a while it got to be torture and it made me try harder to get away. There was another time when Brace was producing a big musical hour and a half for one of the networks and he had me in it singing three numbers. We were rehearsing in a converted theater in the East Fifties, an old newsreel theater. Chuck was due back on this particular day after two weeks in Europe, and Brace was showing all the symptoms. Even from the studio I could see that he wasn't really with it. He was walking in and out of the control room, not paying much attention to what was going on in front of the cameras, and he wasn't chewing the director out but was just letting him do as he pleased, and that was unusual because even when he wasn't directing, Brace would be directing, know what I mean?

It happened to be a color show, which was not too common at the time, and all of a sudden one of the cameras went out of phase. Brace called a break and disappeared. The dressing rooms were downstairs in the basement and there was also a hot coffee machine there, so I went down to check my makeup and to get myself a container. As I walked down the hall toward the coffee machine I looked through the half-open door of the men's dressing room and there was Brace with his back to the door talking into a wall phone. I got my coffee and walked quietly back up the hall until I could hear what he was saying.

"Listen, buddy-boy, I couldn't wait till you got back."

And then, "As soon as I can, baby doll."

And then, like he hadn't planned it before, "I have to call a lunch break for the crew. Suppose I give everybody a long hour and come over to see you for a while."

Then something was said on the other end that made him laugh in an excited kind of way, and I could just imagine what it was because he said, "Don't worry, buddy-boy. I saved it all for you," and hung up.

I ducked into the women's dressing room and stayed there until I heard him go upstairs, and by the time I got back up he had given everybody a two-hour lunch break.

He came over to me and said, "What are you doing for lunch?"

"I thought maybe you and I would grab a bite together," I said.

"I'm not really hungry," he said, not looking me in the eye because his part in this game was him acting like a husband and denying that he was gay. "I want to think about the script. Let's cab over to the apartment and you can eat and rest for a while and I'll walk around a little."

We cabbed over to our building and while he was reaching for change to pay the cabbie and having a hard time finding any, I said, "Where are you going to be?"

"I told you, I'll be walking around!" he said, real snappy. "Now go upstairs and have your lunch."

As soon as I got upstairs and into the apartment, which was less than two minutes later, I looked out the front windows and saw the cab up at the corner waiting for a light I opened the window and leaned out but I couldn't see Brace anywhere. There wasn't a soul on the street and I knew damn well that he couldn't have walked to the corner and gone out of sight that fast, so I looked after the cab and sure enough. I saw it go up the next block and stop in front of Chuck's building.

P.S.: Brace got back to rehearsal one hour late. The director got tired of waiting for him and started the rehearsal without him, and when Brace walked in he looked like he had just showered. He probably had, and he wasn't wearing the same shirt he had left in, which wasn't strange because he always kept some clothes at Chuck's place.

Another thing that bugged the hell out of me was the way Brace was always competing with me. He would compete with me the way one woman competes with another and about the same things, too. First it was the way we dressed. If we were getting ready to go out for an evening, he would always take his shower after I did. Then he would take a long time shaving and laying out his clothes, and by the time I was dressed and ready to go I would have to wait for him, which is a switch in itself, right? All this was to give him time to see what kind of jewelry I was wearing. Once he knew, he would get out the diamond shirt studs, and the cufflinks to match, and we're not talking about diamond chips, let me tell you. And there was his silver identification bracelet which Chuck had given him for his birthday with his name picked out in emeralds which went on one wrist. On the other wrist would be one of his many jeweled watches. And, of course, he never wore less than two rings and sometimes three or four, depending on what I wore. There was the big onyx initial ring that fitted on one pinkie and there was the square-cut topaz for the other pinkie and the opal ring and the diamond-cut emerald if he needed reinforcements. Long before hippies started wearing necklaces, Brace was wearing a silver chain that hung down across his chest, made of very delicate links that caught the light whenever he moved.

The other way he competed with me was over men. Would you believe it? You see I was still human and I wanted to get a little fun out of life, too, so I figured if Brace was making it in his own way, why shouldn't I make it in mine?

I tried to make the scene with every good-looking guy who came my way, and if he happened to be somebody working with or for Brace, then I tried harder, and if he was someone I knew Brace didn't like or hated or who hated him, then I tried extra hard, because I knew the guy would be sure to blab all over the place that he had banged Brace Fontaine's wife and it would get back to Brace and burn his ass. The reason why I wasn't very successful was because Brace always spotted the guy I had my eye on and would try to take him away from me, so help me!

Whenever we went to an affair such as a party or a reception, we would walk in and look the place over and Brace would say something like, "The guy in the cummerbund."

And I would say, "What?"

And he would say, "That guy in the fancy cummerbund. The tall blond guy talking to the little brunette. That's him, right?"

And he would be right. That would be the guy I had spotted and had my eye on, the guy I was going to try to make it with. Only Brace would get there first. And either the guy was gay, or he swung both ways or else he would get embarrassed by the way Brace would butt in while we were dancing together or having a couple of laughs and Brace would start talking and putting on the charm and gradually he would get the guy away from me.

There was an actor named Brad Weston. Brad was a very sweet guy, not terribly good-looking but with a kind of tough, rugged face and I really dug him. He dug me, too. Whenever we would run into one another, we would always sit down and have a cup of coffee together or just talk and walk together down the street, and I guess if there wasn't a Brace something might have come out of it. Anyway, Brad was doing a television police show that Brace was producing. He was playing one of the leads, an older cop with a young, rookie sidekick. Brace used to have Brad over at the apartment once in a while to talk over scripts or to iron out little things that would come up, like personal appearances to boost the show. One evening Brad came over to see Brace but Brace had been held up at the office and wasn't home yet. So Brad and I sat around talking and digging each other like crazy and just having a great time. We got so involved with what we were saying to each other that we never heard Brace come in. All of a sudden he was there looking at us and I knew right away from his face that his brain was one mass of green, because that's the way he was. If he thought he saw another guy trying to make out with me and he knew that the guy was straight and he couldn't get at him, he would get jealous. Well, he saw Brad there with me on the terrace laughing and talking, and we were having such a great time enjoying each other's company that he just had to do something about it.

He started to throw himself at Brad, but really throw himself. I have never seen anything like it. He really was trying to turn Brad on to him. He was trying to make him. He walked up and down the living room wiggling his hips and he smiled at Brad and looked in his eyes and he was pouring drinks into him by the gallon, or trying to but not having much luck because Brad doesn't drink very much. In fact, Brace wasn't having any luck all around, because Brad happens to be straight and has no use for gay men. When it was time for Brad to leave, Brace insisted on driving him home, and after they were gone for about an hour, he called and said that he was still talking to Brad up at Brad's place. Two hours later, Brad brought him home, tanked to the gills and falling all over his feet. We got him into bed and Brad told me that Brace had bought two bottles of wine and had insisted on sitting in his kitchen drinking and talking and trying to make him until finally he drank too much and Brad had to bring him back. We looked at Brace out on the bed and then we looked at each other, and I guess the same thought came into both our minds. I didn't object when Brad put his arm around me and walked me out onto the terrace. It was about three o'clock in the morning on a nice summer night and we lay down on the outdoor chaise behind a lot of shrubs and trees and Brad laid me with Brace snoring away just the other side of the bedroom window. It was a great lay, and for the first time in a long time I had a really good healthy time with a man. When Brad left at about five, I was sorry to see him go because we both knew that Brace would probably never give us another chance like that again. Brace never knew, because Brad is not the kind of a guy who would talk about it to anyone, and it's been a secret between us ever since. Brad got married to a nice girl and when we would meet as we did once in a while, we would smile at each other when we remembered how we put it over on Brace out on the terrace.

If there was one way in which I could not put anything over on Brace, it was with my big plan to make myself independent. Now that I look back, I realize that he and Chuck must have been turning handsprings to keep me tied to him. The last thing in the world those guys wanted was me making it on my own and having enough money to start a divorce action and maybe spilling the beans in open court. Wouldn't the papers have had a field day with a story like that? And what about all the enemies the Happiness Twins had made for themselves at the networks and out in Hollywood, because you don't use power the way they did and not make enemies.

191

By this time Brace, through Chuck, was king of television. He was producing and directing and even writing shows all over the screen. Not only that, he was coming up with new show ideas and, through Chuck, getting them on the networks, and there wasn't a single night during the week when you couldn't tune in to almost any channel and not see his credit at least once. The money coming in was fabulous, because Brace got paid for every one of these things he did. Every show budget had a fee for a producer and one for a writer and for a director, right? And Brace was collecting them all. Not as three separate checks, but in one big check, right? And when you broke the check down into how much the show would have paid three different guys for those jobs, it came up to just a little less. When you have six or seven shows going all at once, it all adds up, buster, and it adds up big. Being conservative I would say that Brace was pulling in about sixty thousand a week at this time. And on top of that he had ownership in every new show that he originated. Now at that time new shows didn't pay off until they'd been on the air at least two and a half seasons. All of Brace's properties had at least a year and a half to two years to run. There was no doubt that they would make it all the way because with two Boy Scouts like Brace and Chuck looking after their own, why shouldn't they, provided they stayed in control. Listen, if you had ever heard the way those two would juggle shows around over the phone like they were picking fruit off a sidewalk pushcart, you wouldn't have any trouble believing me. A lot of ATA shows went off the air because the producer or the star wouldn't play ball or because someone wasn't one of the boys, and you know what that meant.

Brace had put a down payment on a new co-op apartment in U.N. Plaza and he had just hired an architect to build us a hunting and skiing lodge in Canada. The last thing he needed was little me flying out of the nest and breaking all the eggs, so my professional career started to suffer. It was all right for me to appear on a special once in a while, but that was it. Five Star Productions wanted to know if Nina Brandi would like to appear in her own television series. They had a property that would be great for her, a sure winner. Forget it! Nina Brandi wouldn't like to be separated from her husband who had to stay in New York. That was the excuse which, of course, didn't come from me. It came from guess-who's office. MCA thought that with the proper handling Nina Brandi had a great future as an entertainer. Would I like to sign a three-year contract? I would love to, but forget it! Nina Brandi's husband objected to his wife spending so much time away from home and that was that.

There's nothing that can kill a female performer's career like a husband who doesn't want her to have it. All he has to do is to call up her agent or manager two or three times and complain about how much time she has to put in at rehearsals and traveling. And when the husband calls the shots at a major agency, it only takes one phone call, right? I will never forget as long as I live the shock I had the afternoon I walked into the Men's Bar at the Astor to talk to Mike Krantz about an offer he had from a club in Frisco. I saw them just as I was coming in from the lounge, Brace and Mike at the bar. I turned right around and went home and waited for the phone call. It came an hour later.

"I thought we had a date," Mike said.

"We did, but my husband beat me to it," I said.

There was a long pause and then Mike said, "You know, Nina, you're not my only client. And I can't live off the club dates I can get you maybe once a month. After all, most of my people depend on television for their bread. What can I do?"

"Once I asked you to give me away, Mike," I said, with tears coming up into my throat. "I never asked you to sell me out."

"Nina, what can I say?"

"Just say good-bye, Mike," I told him. "That's what I'm saying."

And I hung up.

A week later, Bobby Casey's producer, Jack Hamlin, called me up and asked how I'd like to do the show. Appearing on Bobby's "Manhattan Midnight" was one of the biggest apples in the business. A lot of careers have started with a blast-off on Bobby's show and I knew that it could happen to me. Isn't that always the dream? I didn't have to wait to make up my mind. I said yes. Bobby's show wasn't an agency show and besides he gave ATA's clients valuable exposure time on the air so I knew that Brace or Chuck couldn't put any pressure on Bobby, but to be safe I didn't say a word about it to anyone, not even to Billie or Joye. The afternoon of the taping, I told Brace I would be at the beauty parlor. The show was aired that same night. Brace was working late again, but he must have tuned in to see the show, because thirty seconds after it was over the phone rang, and it was not Brace but Chuck to congratulate me. Brace was too busy to come to the phone, he said, so he was doing the honors for him. I had been sensational. I said thank you and hung up, and I thought about how Gordon must have had to tie Brace down on the bed to keep him from running home and killing me.

But it was true! I had sung and I had talked with Bobby and he had asked me about my sisters and my life since the act had split up, and about my married life and my views about love and marriage and sex and I just let loose, without going too far, of course, and the audience in the studio just lapped it up. And then I had sung again and the studio had come apart and Bobby had said to come again, real soon, which was the signal that he really wanted you back. It made all the columns the next day. George Cobb, always a big fan of mine, put it at the top under a special headline: "Brandi Straight—Nina's Big Moment." The phones started to ring the next day, and all the agents who had never handled me wanted to sign me up and a few who had been scared off by Brace were willing to try again. For a week, I floated off the ground, and then gradually the offers began to fall off and the agents stopped calling and I came back to earth. Brace had won again. Two weeks later, Jack Hamlin called and asked me to stand by for another appearance. Bobby was doing a week of shows in Las Vegas and then he was coming back to New York and he would like me there to help welcome him back.

Two days later the news was in the papers. On his last night in Vegas, Bobby Casey had been accosted by two men outside his hotel room and beaten up. The two men came out of an elevator which was held for them by a third, and after the beating, they stepped back into the elevator and disappeared. Bobby spent two days in a hospital while someone else stood in for him. There was no statement to the press but the day Bobby got back, Hamlin called me in the morning and said that Bobby had been going over his schedule of guests and, sorry, but there were a few who hadn't made it once yet, and he knew that I would understand. Maybe next season. He would call.

I cried about it for a day, and then I forgot because something else came up to occupy my mind. For the second time in my life, I was pregnant.

Chapter
SEVENTEEN

The first thing Brace said when I told him was, "Don't tell Chuck!" So, of course, I made sure that Chuck knew as fast as I could get the news to him. The day after the expectant father was aware that he was expectant, and he wasn't exactly busting out with cigars all over the place when he heard the news, we were out with Gordon and Joye and Sam at "21", and George Cobb table-hopped over to us.

He went the rounds pumping each of us for items for his column. When he got to Brace he got a rundown on all the television productions Brace had a finger in, and then he turned to me and said, "What about you, Nina? Has Brace got a part in any of these productions for you?"

"I've got a production of my own started," I told him, and I felt Brace who was sitting next to me go stiff. Gordon looked up and Brace kicked me under the table, but nothing was going to stop me now because I could see that Gordon was looking at me with a kind of amused smile on his face.

"Don't tell me you've got a series," George said, looking at me very curiously. "What is this, another husband-wife producing team?"

"You hit the nail right on the head, George," I told him. "Only it's not a series. It's a one-shot. I went into production about two months ago. It'll take another seven months to produce. And I hope it's a boy!"

I saw the smile slip off Gordon's face and he went white, dead-white. He looked at Brace with such a hurt, surprised expression on his face that I almost felt sorry for him.

George said, "Good for you, Nina! And congratulations, Brace! Is this for the record?"

"For the record," I told him, and Gordon got up and left the table and Joye got up and put her arms around me and Sam shook Brace's hand and kissed me and Brace looked after Gordon, very upset, and got up and followed him. After a minute, I went to the powder room and on the way I walked through the bar looking for them but they weren't there. Then I spotted them in a phone booth. Gordon was sitting in the booth making believe he was waiting for a call, I guess, and Brace was standing in the door of the booth.

Gordon looked haggard and he was saying to Brace in a very upset voice so that I could hear it, "But you promised me it would never happen! You promised!"

To tell you the truth, I was pretty surprised myself. After all, when you and your husband only get together in bed once every two weeks and he spends more time down on you than in you, you really don't expect much to come out of it, right? Well, something had, and it wasn't because of Brad Weston because that had happened a long time before and there hadn't been anybody else since, so it had to be Brace.

Brace didn't know how to take it. I could see that he didn't care for the idea of being a father again but there wasn't a damn thing he could do about it this time. We were married and he had to go along with it, like it or not. One thing he did do was to stop sex. But completely! When his regular night came around again he stayed up watching the "Late Show." And when I said something like, let's go to bed and get it over with because I'm tired, he said that he couldn't touch me anymore, not with a baby in me. It might hurt the baby, he said. I had to laugh but it didn't bother me because I was just as happy not having to put up with his sick idea of sex. I had my baby growing inside of me and this time I knew that I didn't have to lose it and that I would see it born and hold it in my arms and that was enough for me.

Alan Stone was very happy for me. Of course I had gone to him as soon as I was sure, and he had examined me and made the usual tests and when the answer came back he said, "You're one hundred percent right, Nina. It's a baby."

He thought that having the baby would do me a lot of good. We had had a couple of talks before this because once or twice I had felt very down and I had taken him up on his word and gone to see him about it. We had discussed Brace and Chuck and what my life was like and why; since he was my doctor, I felt I could talk to him and not feel ashamed or afraid that it would get back to Brace. He used words like sadistic and masochistic, which I had heard before but never really understood, and he explained them to me, in his kind, friendly way, so that I

196

understood them. I came away from these talks understanding Brace a little better and more convinced that unless he changed, which didn't seem likely, I would have to get myself and the baby away from him.

I told my mother the good news, of course, and my sisters, and they were all very happy about it. Marcie and Angie had children of their own by this time. Dolores was still with my mother, only they weren't living in Brooklyn anymore because Dolores had gone into the real estate business. She had taken a night course and then the state test and gotten her license as a real estate broker. She was doing pretty well, too. She opened a small office in Rockland County, which was having a big real estate boom, and after a while she made enough money to buy the house in Haverstraw. It was an old farmhouse but in good condition and she and Mom moved up there so Dolores could be close to her business. Mom wasn't feeling well at the time. We didn't know just what was bothering her and the doctors didn't seem to know either. She wasn't looking too good when she came down to the city to see me, but I think just the idea that I was having a baby of my own did her a lot of good and after that first visit she came down every week to stay with me for a few days.

I started to fix up a nursery in the apartment. We had more rooms than we knew what to do with, with a study for Brace and a TV room and a hi-fi room and a library with a lot of books that Brace had bought but that we never read, and a maid's room.

I had the hi-fi hooked up in the living room and then I had the nursery painted all white and pink and blue with new curtains on the windows. I went to Lord and Taylor's and bought a crib and a bassinet and a chest of drawers with pink bunnies painted on them and had them put in the room. Joye was very busy finishing up her book so she didn't have much time for lunch and long talks anymore, but she came to see the nursery one day. She wouldn't tell me about the book. All she would say was, "Wait and see. You'll be surprised." Brace wasn't as close to them as he once was, maybe because of the kickback which I think hurt Sam, because after all it was he who had helped Brace get started in the television business and introduced him to Gordon in the first place. But the Garricks were still glad that we were having a baby, because I think they still thought of Brace as a kind of son, and when I told them that they would be the baby's godparents, that made them very happy.

Brace tried not to pay any attention to what was going on, but when the nursery was all fixed up he stood in the doorway looking at it and when he turned away there was a funny kind of expression on his face. He was spending as much time as he could away from the apartment and me, I could see that, but I began to have the feeling that he wasn't with Chuck so much but more with his shows. They must have had a couple of fights, because there were times when Brace would come home early and mope around the apartment and eat his dinner without talking to me and sit around all evening watching television. And then I guess they would make up because he would get very happy and cheerful and he would call Chuck and have long conversations with him over the phone. I caught part of what he was saying one day, and it sounded like the "baby doll" and "buddy-boy" routine all over again.

I started to show in the fourth month and went into maternity clothes and Brace made a big fuss about that. He said he couldn't go out with me looking like that, even if I was wearing maternity evening gowns, and the more pregnant I looked the more irritable he got with me. But the first time I felt life, I was lying in bed one morning; and when I felt it, I needed someone to share the moment with me, so I took his hand and put it on my stomach. He looked horrified and pulled it away but he must have felt something too, because he looked amazed and put his hand back, very hesitant, like he was afraid something might bite it, and the baby moved again and that same strange expression came over his face like when he looked at the nursery.

For New Year's we went down to Miami for a week because Brace was producing a benefit show for a Jewish charity at the Saxony. I didn't want to go because a day or two before Angie had called to tell me that the doctors had finally diagnosed what was bothering Mom, and it was cancer. It was in the area of the pancreas and they weren't sure how bad it was or if they could operate or if they should, and I was very upset about it.

But Jewish people are big family people, right? And Brace couldn't show up without his wife because how would that look, so I had to go to save my husband's image. There were a lot of stars on the bill and a lot of celebrities and well-known men and women from many professions in the audience. I sat at a table with some Hollywood stars and it was a very gala occasion. Toward the end of the bill they started playing the big follow spot around the audience picking out the celebrities and the spot picked up somebody at my table and the spill caught me. Someone recognized me and said, "What about Nina Brandi?"

And someone else called out, "Yeah, what about Nina Brandi? Let her take a bow."

Brace had just come back from backstage and joined me at the table and he tried to look pleased; the spot fell on me and I stood up and took a bow, and a lot of people applauded when the emcee said, "There's Nina Brandi, formerly of the Brandi Sisters. You remember the Brandi Sisters, folks."

"Of course we remember," a little old lady at a ringside table said to him. "She used to sing 'Eli, Eli.'"

Which was correct. Just before the Ellis show we had played the Borscht Belt on a summer tour of the hotels. A lot of entertainers who are big names now were playing the Catskills at the time, people like Jack Carter and Milton Berle and Sid Caesar. It was a rough routine because in one evening you would play maybe three or four hotels going from one to the other in a bus. We went over very big up there, and one of the things the audiences loved was our closing medley in which we sang a lot of their favorites, like "Bei Mir Bist Du Shoen" and the "Beer Barrel Polka" and "Eli, Eli," which I sang in Yiddish. It was my father's idea and it was brilliant, because it was a real show-stopper. And we would top it with "God Bless America" for a finale that brought down the house again. Two show-stoppers in a row. Well, this little old lady must have been at one of the hotels at the time and she remembered Nina Brandi singing "Eli, Eli." And a lot of other people remembered too, because the little old lady said, "Come on, Nina. Sing 'Eli, Eli' for us," and they started to applaud and the applause grew and Brace didn't know what to do or say and people started calling out "Eli, Eli." After all, this was a Jewish affair, right?

Brace looked sick when the emcee came over to take me by the hand and lead me onto the floor. Brace didn't like seeing me in the spotlight one bit. The band played me an intro and some of them must have been Borscht Belt graduates themselves, because as I sang a solo sax came in and played behind me very softly as though we had rehearsed it. I was almost overwhelmed finding myself up in front of an audience without any warning, and I started a little weakly. Then I felt the audience responding and the light shining on me and the old performer took over and my voice came out clear and strong with all that brassy quality lifting up the old tear-jerking Jewish melody like a trumpet. And I thought about what the song was saying and about my mother, and by the time I ended up on that strong loud note at the end and held it, there were tears on my cheeks and the audience was up on its feet cheering the place down.

Then Brace came forward and tried to lead me off and he almost killed it for me, but the applause went on and on and they wouldn't let me go, so he had to bring me back.

We stood there taking a bow together and the noise was really deafening. Then we went off and he disappeared. I thanked the bandleader and then I went back to the table and sat there talking to the other people and waiting for Brace. We were supposed to go out to supper together. After an hour had passed and he still hadn't come back, I had the maître d' page him backstage and in the lobby and after a while a bellhop came over to the table with a note for me. It was from the desk clerk. My husband had checked out and gone back to New York.

I went back to our room and it was true. His clothes and his luggage were gone and my airline ticket was lying on the desk. We were supposed to spend the rest of the week in Miami, but I guess my "Eli, Eli" was too much for him. That *was* the reason, as I found out when I got back to New York. The story was in *Variety*, and the columns. All he could talk about was how I had made a fool out of him and made him look like an idiot in front of all these people by taking the show away from him. It was then that I realized how jealous he was of me and why I was dead with all the agents. It wasn't just to keep me from upsetting his little applecart at the networks. He was afraid that any success I had as an entertainer would make him look bad. And now after he had done everything he could to kill my career, I had the nerve to grab the spotlight away from him not once but twice, first by having a baby and then by stopping the show at the Saxony.

He had very little to do with me after that until we went to Palm Springs. He had to supervise a new pilot that was being shot there on location nearby and he was going to be gone for a week so he insisted that I come along, too. I guess that after the "Eli, Eli" thing, he felt he couldn't trust me to just stay put, baby or no baby, and he would have been right, too, because the way he was acting was convincing me more and more that I had to get away from him.

We stayed at a very swank motel with a main guest house and airconditioned cottages near the pool, with palm trees and cactus plants and a golf course. We took a room close to the pool so I wouldn't have far to walk in the heat to take a swim because I wasn't going to go out on location in the desert and sit around all day watching Brace and a lot of actors horse around in that broiling sun.

The first night we were there who should turn up and take over one of the cottages but Freddie Manners, with one gofer, three broads, and his golf clubs. By this time he had split up with Dorey Allen because, according to the grapevine in the business, Dorey's wife couldn't stand having Freddie and his girls hanging around all the time. Anyway, I came into the lobby on my way to the magazine stand to pick out a magazine while he was registering and he saw me and said, "Jesus Christ! Even in the fucking desert."

I didn't pay any attention to him, but for the rest of the time we were there, he paid a lot of attention to me. At night I'd be in the cottage watching television while Brace was off somewhere looking at the dailies or talking to his director about the next day's shooting, and Freddie would park his car out in front and bang one of the girls where I could hear and see what was going on.

He used to talk to the broad at the top of his lungs first and then he would snort and pant and yell, "God, this is magnificent!" and "Jesus, baby, send me again." Or else, "Go down, doll. Go down!" And if I looked out the window or went out to look at the stars, there he'd be banging away on the back seat. Finally, one day, I grabbed his gofer as he was passing by and I said, "Look, tell Freddie he's got a great little act going out there. Tell him that I'm getting a big laugh watching his big fat ass waving around under the desert moon."

He didn't do it again, not in front of my window he didn't.

At the end of the week, Brace called up Chuck the last night we were there to tell him about how the shooting went. They had a big lovey-dovey conversation for a while behind Brace's hand and then they started to talk about cars. I had been after Brace to get me my own car. We had the convertible and the Caddy and a chauffeur to drive us around in style, but I wanted a smaller car so I could get around by myself if I wanted to and park without any trouble and take off to see Mom whenever I felt like it without tying up the chauffeur. I had decided on an English Ford and Brace had promised to buy one for me for our next anniversary, but now as he was talking to Chuck I heard them talking about a Mercedes and how Chuck was crazy about his, and I heard Brace telling him that he was going to get me one.

After he hung up, I said to him, "What's this about a Mercedes?"

"Didn't I tell you?" he said like it had slipped his mind. "I'm buying you one."

"I don't want a Mercedes," I said. "I want an English Ford."

"A Mercedes is a better car," he said.

"I don't want a Mercedes," I said. "I want an English Ford."

"Chuck Gordon is driving a Mercedes and he says it's a great car and that's what you're getting."

"I don't care what Chuck Gordon says. I want an English Ford."

"You're getting a Mercedes."

"Why do I have to have what Chuck Gordon likes? Why can't I have what I like?"

"Because I'm buying it for you and I'm buying you a Mercedes. If it's good enough for Chuck, I don't see why it can't be good enough for you."

It had been a bad day. The baby was pressing on a nerve or something and I wasn't feeling too well, and this stupid argument was going around in circles.

"Fuck Chuck Gordon!" I said. "I want an English Ford."

"You're getting a Mercedes!"

"I won't take it! I won't drive it!"

"You'll take it! And you'll drive it! What's the matter with you? Just because Chuck Gordon—!"

"That's right!" I said. "Just because Chuck Gordon! Because I've had about all I can stand of Chuckee-boy. That sonofabitch has had his prick in my marriage and in my bed and now he's sticking it in my car! Well, you can go take your fucking Mercedes and shove it up Chuckee-boy's ass!"

"Look out, Nina. Don't start that again!"

"On second thought, how can you shove the Mercedes up his ass when you're always up there?"

He slapped me across the face hard, back and forth.

"Shut up!" he yelled at me, and slapped me again.

"Go ahead!" I yelled back. "Go ahead. Slap me! Punch me! Hit me some more! You like to knock women around, you lousy fag! Now's your chance to knock a pregnant woman around!"

He had his hand up in the air again but when he heard that pregnant line, he brought it down and held it with his other hand. Then he shoved his finger in my face and said, "Don't you mention his name again! You mention his name again and I'll kill you!"

My head was ringing from his slaps and I could feel a trickle of blood from my nose, but I wouldn't shut up. I was like a punchdrunk fighter still on his feet after the referee calls the match.

"I'll say it all I want!" I screamed. "Gordongordongordongordongordongordongordongordon . . ." And I went on and on and he stared at me and then he turned and ran over to the night table on his side of the bed and opened the drawer. I knew what he was getting. He always carried a .38 revolver whenever we traveled because of my jewelry. It was always kept in his night table with the bullet clip out so there couldn't be any accidents. He took the gun out and I saw him load it, and then he crossed to me and jammed it up against my heart and said, "Now! You open your mouth once more and you've had it!"

I looked him in the eye. He had that deadpan expression on his face and his eyes were staring right into mine without blinking and I knew that he meant it.

I said to myself, don't say a word, but I opened my mouth and said, "You win. For the sake of the baby."

He stared at me and the deadpan expression went into a dull kind of look. He dropped his eyes and turned away and put the gun down on the night table and then he lay down with his face in his hands. He lay there like that for a long time and I stood where he had left me without moving for a long time. Then we went to bed without saying another word to each other, with the gun still on the night table. And it was still there the next morning.

Chapter
EIGHTEEN

We checked out of the motel and drove to the airport and flew home and went back to our apartment without saying a word to each other. The gun was between us as though it was there lying on the car seat and on the seat in the plane, right there between us, and I could still feel it where he had pressed it into me hard and round. He had a hard, sullen look on his face and he stared out of the car window and he stared out of the plane window and then out of the window of the cab driving into Manhattan from Kennedy, just staring into space and not moving a muscle of his face. I don't even think he moved his eyelids, though I guess that would be impossible.

I think that maybe he was a little frightened of himself, of what he almost did, because that night, as we were getting ready to go to bed, he looked at my tummy, which was pretty big by then because I was in my seventh month already, and he said, "I could have killed you, do you know that? You and the baby!" At first he sounded like he was saying that it was my fault, that if he had pulled the trigger I would have been the one to blame, but his voice went up at the end in a question mark as though he didn't want to believe that he really could have killed me.

I went into my eighth month with Brace away on the coast with Chuck Gordon and Mom getting ready to go into the hospital for an operation. Joye's book was in at the publisher's but she was still too busy to visit. We spoke on the phone once or twice and she said that she was now writing a screen treatment of the book so she could be all ready to write the screenplay as soon as the book made the best-seller list, but I knew that was just an excuse. I had the feeling for some reason she didn't want to see me but I couldn't figure out why.

Brace came back from Hollywood with the fall lineup all ready to go; three of the new shows would have his logo on them. He had incorporated himself, which was supposed to give him a better deal taxwise. At this time, the agency was trying to fade into the background of the television business because people were starting to ask questions and talking about an F.C.C. investigation. It was getting to the point where he and Chuck had almost run their setup into the ground, and they were trying to keep it alive, only I didn't know that.

We were still not talking to each other very much but the first night he was home he came into the nursery where I was putting a cover on the crib mattress and he held out a box and said, "I brought back something for the baby."

I opened the box and there was one of those goofy, cute hanging toys that go over a crib, with birds and fish floating around in the air on wires and springs.

The gun bit was still fresh in my mind, along with the one-two slaps he had handed out to me that night, and I said, "The baby won't be ready for anything like that for months after it's born."

"How would you know?" he said, and he took it out of my hands. "After all, this is only your first."

And then he remembered something and I did too and he looked at me and then quickly away and went and got a chair and a thumbtack and hung the toy up over the crib from the ceiling. I watched him do it and I could see by the way he was getting the toy to hang, so that it bounced up and down just right, that this was a very special thing for him. It was the first time that he had shown interest in the baby. In fact, it was the first time that he was acting like he had actually had something to do with it in the first place. After the toy was hanging right, he made the little birds go around and around and he seemed to get a real charge out of it.

"The things they make for kids these days," he said, and then he acted like he had made a slip because he gave the toy a hard swat so that the birds flew around like sixty, and he left the room.

After that at least once a week he came home with something for the baby, which he said he got from people on his crews or from people at the office who gave them to him to give to me, but I knew that was a lot of crap, and after a while he stopped using excuses and just brought the things home. There were Disney wall plaques to hang around the nursery, and contraptions that you tied to the crib sides and hung across the baby with teething rings and bells on them, and little hand rattles for the baby to shake and a box of baby soaps in the form of little animals, and bolsters for the crib, which was a very practical idea that I hadn't even thought of because, as he said, this was my first baby.

About the middle of that month Mom went into Good Samaritan Hospital in Suffern for her operation. Angie phoned me after it was over and told me that they had opened her up and found that it was too advanced to take it out. The doctor said it was a slow-growing cancer and it would take months until it killed her. He said they would try some X-ray or cobalt treatments when she was a little better. She didn't know, of course, and there wasn't a thing any of us could do for her except keep her as happy as possible for as long as she was around. I sat up and cried, and when Brace came home after midnight and found me still crying, he said not to worry, that Mom would have the best of care and that he would pay for the X-ray or cobalt or whatever else they wanted to try.

At the beginning of the ninth month, Billie threw me a baby shower. She told me I was letting myself go to pot and she made me go to a beauty parlor, and while I was out everybody sneaked in and surprised me when I got back. Brace came home while the shower was still going on but he didn't look annoyed or anything, and after dinner he let the maid have the rest of the evening off and helped me put away the loot that the baby had collected.

Most of it went into the chest of drawers in the nursery, and when we were finished he stood in the middle of the room looking around and said, "I wonder if my mother ever did things like this for me before I was born." And then he shrugged and said, "Probably not. She never had any dough until she collected my old man's settlement. And then she took off with it."

He talked a little about his childhood that night while we were sitting around. It was the first time in a long time, the first time since our pre-engagement, before we were kicked out of my mother's house, that we had sat and talked like that. He told me about his aunt and how she hated his mother for running away and leaving her saddled with him. And he told me how she took it out on him and beat him and shut him up in the cellar when he was only two years old because he had wet his pants.

He changed a lot during that month. It was like after the beating he had given me with the pocketbook when we had a second honeymoon. This time he had come that close to shooting me but it seemed like it was a kind of crisis for him, and when it passed he was over it and something in him had been let go—steam, maybe.

He had gotten to like holding his hand on my stomach and feeling the baby move and kick, and he went to the library and got out a book that showed all the different stages of how a baby develops and he spent one evening sitting at home looking at the pictures and saying, "That's how he looks right now."

Like me, he was sure it would be a boy, and he told me what he was going to do for his son, because now the baby was "his son," get it? I think what he had in mind was giving the kid the kind of childhood he felt he had been cheated out of, only I asked myself while he was talking: How could a queer like him ever give a child a normal, healthy home?

He also spent a lot of time talking to Chuck on the phone. He seemed to be trying to convince him that everything was all right, and once I heard him say, "Now don't be silly, buddy-boy. It will still be the same. We'll go on just like we always have. He won't make that much difference, you'll see." I knew that the "he" they were talking about was the baby, and I said to myself that they could go on in the same old way all they liked but not around my baby.

That ninth month was pretty bad for me because I started developing complications. My feet swelled and my kidneys started acting up, and Alan made me spend the last two weeks in the hospital in bed until the baby came. Brace was at the hospital visiting when I went into labor and when the pains started and the nurse came in to check me and Alan showed up to stand by, he began to act in a very funny way. It was like all of a sudden he didn't want the baby to be born, like he was trying to stall for time while he thought of something to say or do, as though Chuck Gordon was more on his mind than me and the baby that was coming, and that was his.

The pains got worse and the nurses wanted to take me to the labor room, but Brace kept talking to me and getting in their way, laughing and putting on an act like it was a false alarm.

"This is her first one," he told Alan. "She's not going to deliver that fast. What's all the fuss?"

"It's just that there are some minor complications," Alan told him, trying to keep his voice professional and calm. "I'd rather have her in the labor room where I've got everything I might need right at hand."

"Ah, you doctors are all alike," Brace said. "Always running scared. Like having a baby wasn't the most natural thing in the world! I know you're earning your fee, Doctor. You don't have to sell me!"

Finally, they got him out into the hall and Alan had me put on the cart and wheeled out. As I went down the hall, I heard one of the nurses say to Brace, "The waiting room is at the end of the corridor, Mr. Fontaine! You'll find a couple of other expectant fathers pacing there."

"I don't pace!" was Brace's answer, and he went back to his office.

Delivering me turned out to be pretty complicated because the baby had to be turned, and when it was over and he was born I started to hemorrhage and my blood pressure went down to zero and they had to sweat over me in the recovery room until they got it back up. When I came to and I could look around, I saw Alan next to the bed with a mask over his nose. Brace was with him, with a mask on too, and he said he had seen the baby and it was a big, healthy boy.

Brace came to the hospital every day to see me and once or twice they let him hold the baby. He acted just like any other father and that old romantic notion began to float around in the back of my head. Alan dropped in every day to check me out, and I told him about Brace and asked him if a baby could make that much difference.

He said he didn't know for sure one way or the other but maybe it could, and that you could never tell with people like Brace. He said that the interesting thing would be to see how Gordon took the baby and how it affected his relationship with Brace.

My sisters came to see me but Mom couldn't come so she sent her love. Angie said Mom wanted to see the baby in the worst way, and to come to stay with me and help me take care of him until I was back on my feet, but she was still not very strong after the operation. Joye and Sam showed up with flowers and a big box of my favorite candy. Since they were the godparents they were allowed to hold the baby a little, and Sam called the baby "Ace" and told him that he dug everything about babies and then he almost dropped him he got so carried away. Chuck never came near me or the baby while I was in the hospital. He sent me a big bouquet of flowers and I told the nurse to look it over carefully for poison ivy or broken glass or something else nice and unexpected.

Alan wanted to make sure that my kidneys were back to normal and that everything else was working right, so he kept me in the hospital for two weeks after the delivery, and of course Danny had to stay too because I was nursing him. Daniel was what I decided to call him, because, knowing this world the way I did, I figured he was coming into a lion's den.

When I got home there was a special nurse for the baby, of course, and I didn't have to do very much except nurse Danny. For a while Brace looked very proud, and I was told that he went around the network handing out cigars except in Gordon's office, where he never mentioned the baby. I got this from Joye who got it from Sam who got it from his friends at the network. Joye's book was on the presses now, but she was still interested in Chuck Gordon and Brace and we talked about what kind of difference the baby might make between them. Chuck didn't come to see me after I got home from the hospital either, but he did send Danny a gift, a gorgeous English pram which he had ordered from Harrod's in London; it cost him a fortune getting it through customs.

Brace came home one night and said that he was going to throw a big christening party for Danny. He had talked to Goldie about it because it would be at the Show Stoppers and he was going to invite everybody in show business, including all the network brass. It was going to be Danny's birth announcement to the world, he said, but at the same time I could see where it was going to be a big prestige thing for Brace and I wondered if Chuck didn't have something to worry about. You see, even though I was hoping that maybe Brace was changing by some miracle and Danny and I might wind up with a husband and father after all, I still wasn't one hundred percent sure, because I could remember, like they had happened yesterday, all the things Brace had done to me.

Once the baby was home from the hospital, Brace started playing both sides of the fence. When he was home he would spend a half hour every night after dinner in the nursery looking at Danny in his crib and making noises at him, but he would never stay in the room with me when I nursed him. He always made some excuse to be in another part of the apartment or else he had to go out to do something like walk the dog or buy *Variety*. When the nurse brought me the baby in the middle of the night he would turn on his side with his back to me and grumble about not getting his sleep. He still spent at least two nights a week out either at the health club or at Gordon's place, probably holding Chuck's hand and telling him that

209

everything was just like it was, only of course it wasn't and he knew it and so did Chuck.

When Danny was two months old, we took him to church for the christening and gave him his middle name and Sam held him and shushed him when he cried as the cold water hit him in the face. Then we brought him back home and gave him to his nurse and got ready for his christening party which Brace had arranged for that night. He had taken over the entire Show Stoppers, all six rooms. There was a big blow-up of Danny's hospital picture in every room, and three bands, and the place was knee deep in champagne and liquor. Fifteen hundred people showed up, some of them all the way from the coast and from Chicago and Dallas and Miami. Brace had hired a lot of network talent to dance and sing for us and the comics made cracks about this being a command performance because the command was perform or starve, and the songs were all dedicated to me or to Danny and some of the talent on the guest list got up and did their bit too, and it went on for hours.

Brace kept on running from room to room supervising the wine and liquor and meeting and talking to people because the joint was loaded with celebrities and stars and network brass, and if the Chinese or somebody had dropped a bomb on the Show Stoppers that night they would have wiped out American show business and ruled the world, right? I was floating around myself and having a ball because it was my first party in months and months and the champagne was great and I was feeling no pain. Sometime before midnight, I heard people saying that Chuck had just showed up, and I wandered out toward the cloakroom and, sure enough, there he was with some baby-faced broad on his arm. Whether he meant to or not, he passed me right by like I wasn't there and went on into the main dining room. I followed behind and I saw Brace come over and they talked together for a while, and I saw Brace pour him a glass of bourbon on the rocks and then go to the buffet table and make up a plate for him while a waiter served the girl, and I could see that nothing between them had really changed, Danny or no Danny. I saw Chuck look around like he was looking for someone and I was pretty sure he was looking for me, because after all he couldn't come to a party for Brace's kid without saying at least hello to the little lady who had carried the ball across the goal line, could he? Then Brace saw me and came over to get me and led me up to the great man, and Chuck kissed me on the cheek and told me how happy he was for us both, but his eyes kept sliding off mine and he looked like he was trying to focus on anybody else but me.

I got away from him and floated around for a while longer and I was just about starting to feel tired and ready to chicken out and go home, when a hand grabbed my arm and I turned around and there was Chuck, holding on to a glass of bourbon and looking a little tight.

"Hey, Nina, I'd like to talk to you," he said.

"Sure, talk away, Chuck," I told him.

"Over here," he said, and he pulled me into a corner.

He hemmed me in against the wall and then he started to talk about how much Brace meant to him as a business associate and as a friend and about how he knew that Brace meant a lot to me, too, especially now that he was the father of my child and about how the three of us should try to get along together like a team so we could all be happy.

I let him go along like this for a while and finally I said, "Well, that's all right, Chuck. I know that we each have our place in Brace's life. I can understand that. I just don't think that we should try to butt into each other's territory, if you know what I mean."

He looked at me and he started to laugh and I said, "What's so funny?"

"It's funny," he said, controlling his laughter, "because you're talking as though we were equals and we're really not."

"I don't know what you mean," I said.

"What I mean is this," and he leaned closer so that no one else could hear. "Even though you're married to him, I'm the only one who can give him what he wants. Don't forget, baby, I take it up the ass from him and in the mouth, too. That's something you can't give him. I know that you've tried, I know that, and I have to admire you for trying, because you put up a good fight, but when it comes right down to it, you just can't give him what I can give him, right?"

I was stunned for a minute because I never dreamed that he would actually pull the whole thing between us out into the open like that, and for a minute I didn't know what to say. And all of a sudden it hit me. I knew just how to answer him, and it was so obvious I felt like an idiot for not seeing it before.

"You're wrong, Chuck," I said. "And you want to know

211

how wrong? Just look around you. You know what this is all for, don't you? It's for Brace's baby. Something he wanted, I think, very badly. And you know who gave it to him? I did, Chuck. I gave him something you couldn't give him no matter where you take it from him. I gave him a baby. I gave him a son. Right, Chuckee-boy?"

I couldn't resist throwing his queen name at him and I knew by his face that I had hit the bull's eye.

First he went white and then his face got all red and I saw his lips draw back like he was snarling, only the sound that came out of him was no snarl. It was more like a sob, like he had been holding it back a long time and now it was coming out.

"You goddamn bitch," he said, and he sounded hysterical and his voice went up so that some people standing near him heard and turned around. "You goddamn lousy cunt—" And then he went for me. His hands went straight out in front of him and then they were around my throat and I hit at his face with my fists. Somebody came over and tried to pull us apart but it took a couple of people to get his hands off my neck. Then someone called for Brace and he came and tried to calm both of us down, but Chuck was crying and sobbing and carrying on and I was cursing at him and trying to get at him. By this time the word had spread that Chuck Gordon and Nina Fontaine were having a slugging match, and people were crowding around to see. Brace tried to get Chuck to go with him to one of the men's rooms; he had him by the arm and was trying to lead him away when all of a sudden Gordon made a lunge and broke away and headed for the street door, crying and screaming something that no one could understand. Brace took off after him and I went after him too because Chuck was coming apart at the seams, really coming apart, and I wanted to watch him do it.

When I got out into the street I saw them heading toward Fifth Avenue with Chuck trying to get away and Brace right behind him trying to grab him by the arm. I ran after them and caught up to them at the corner.

"What's the matter, Chuckee?" I yelled into his ear. "Didn't your father ever tell you? You can't make babies up the ass!"

He turned and looked at me with tears streaming down his face and he screamed at me, "Get away from me, you cunt! Leave me alone!"

"Nina, for Christ's sake, go back to the party," Brace shouted at me. "Don't you see he's half off his rocker."

"And you're a traitor!" Gordon said, turning on Brace. "You betrayed me, you sonofabitch. You've ruined my life."

Brace had Gordon by one arm now and a little crowd of people was starting to form around us. Then Gordon broke away again and Brace ran after him and they were out in the middle of Fifth Avenue. It wasn't quite twelve o'clock yet and the street was still jammed with taxis and buses and they were dodging around through the traffic and horns were blowing and people on the sidewalks were stopping to watch. I ran after them and caught up with them on the opposite sidewalk. Brace had grabbed Gordon again and was trying to get him into a cab that was waiting at the curb.

The driver was watching and saying, "That's no way to handle a drunk, mister. You want I should give you a hand?"

I got Chuck by the other arm and he swung around to look at me and he groaned and said to Brace, "It's your fucking wife again! Get her away from me."

"The trouble with you, Chuckee," I said, "is that you don't have it between the legs. That's why you always have to take it the other way."

"Nina, get the hell out of here!" Brace snarled at me. "You're only making it worse." He was hanging on to Gordon now with both hands, and the cabbie got disgusted and drove off and Brace let go with one hand to wave at another cab and Gordon broke away again.

This time I got to him before Brace and he and I dodged up the sidewalk between the pedestrians for about a block before Brace caught up and in that block I let go at him with all the anger and the frustration and pain that I had felt inside of me for so long. I tried to pay him back for every punch and slap and bruise and cut that I had ever taken from Brace because of him. He turned on me just as Brace got to us and tried to get his hands on me again but I twisted away and a couple of people tried to grab him and he turned and ran into that bookstore with the circular staircase where the men hang around all day watching the girls go up and down.

Brace cursed and glared at me and followed him in. I stood on the sidewalk out of breath watching what was going on inside. I saw Brace corner Gordon and try to talk to him, but Gordon got away from him and started up the staircase with Brace trying to grab him again. Then a couple of salesmen came over and they tried to catch both Gordon and Brace, and Gordon came back down the stairs with Brace and the salesmen after him. Gordon's hair was all mussed up and he looked wild, and when Brace and the other two tried to corner him again he tried to climb the shelves and knocked down a lot of books. By this time there was quite a crowd watching all this from the sidewalk, and then a cop pushed through and went in and he grabbed Gordon and led him outside with Brace trying to talk to him. I saw Brace take out his wallet and start to show the cop something and then the cop had him by the arm too and a squad car pulled up and Brace and Gordon had to get into the back and the car drove off with them.

Suddenly I felt completely washed out, so I hailed a cab and went home without bothering to go back to the party.

Brace did not come home that night. The story broke in the afternoon papers on the first inside page with pictures of Brace and Gordon arguing on Fifth Avenue and the scene inside the bookstore. Some camera fiend who happened to be there was fast enough to shoot almost a whole roll, and whatever the papers didn't use, he sold to *Life*. That afternoon I heard a news item on WHN about the Board of Directors of the American Talent Agency meeting to consider asking for Charles Gordon's resignation.

Brace didn't come home at all that day or the next, and the *Times* ran a story on the front page which told how Charles Gordon, president of ATA, had had an argument with Mrs. Brace Fontaine which had developed into a brawl in which Brace Fontaine, one of the agency's busiest clients, had joined and about how the bookstore had been torn apart by Mr. Gordon and how both he and Mr. Fontaine had landed in the lockup on charges of disorderly conduct and disturbing the peace, malicious mischief, and trying to bribe a police officer. The story ended by saying the agency's lawyers had gotten the last charge dropped, and that both men were out on bail. *Variety* came out the same day, and they must have held the presses because the big headline on the front page said "ATA Prexy Braced on Fifth Avenue." And there was a big story describing the incident as a lover's quarrel and saying how Gordon and Brace and I were a triangle and then it went on to a rundown of Brace's shows then on the network and how the F.C.C. was now interested in ATA's connections with the networks and the agency board of directors was asking for Chuck's resignation.

Brace came home on the third day, looking as if he hadn't been out of his clothes all that time. I was in the living room with the nurse and Danny, and I was just about to take him into the bedroom to feed him when the front door opened and there was Brace standing in the doorway, staring at me. I started to say something and then I saw that deadpan expression on his face, and I told the nurse to take Danny into the nursery.

She got out of the room just as Brace said, "Goddamn cunt! I'm going to kill you!" He followed me around the living room trying to catch me and I ran out and down the hall to the bedroom and closed the door and tried to hold it shut, but he shoved it open and came after me. I dodged around the bed and he threw himself across the bed and grabbed me. He pulled me to the floor and I got out one scream before he put a hand across my mouth and pulled me up to my feet by one hand around my throat. Then he threw me down on the bed and I got my breath and screamed. There was a belt lying across the back of my dressing table chair. It had a cut diamond buckle and it went with a lamé evening gown. He saw it and grabbed it and started to swing it at me. I screamed again and I heard the nurse run screaming into the hall and then the buckle cut into one of my legs.

I tried to scramble up the bed to get away from him and he followed alongside, hitting me across the legs with the belt, and each time the buckle landed it cut into my flesh. Then he started aiming for my face and I threw my arms up and it was like I was trying to get away from my father again when he had lost his temper. The buckle hit me across the arms and shoulders and once it caught me across the cheek and I felt the blood trickling down and I screamed, "Stop, Daddy! Daddy, please stop! Daddy, don't! Please don't hit me, Daddy!" I felt that I was going to be killed and I got off the bed and tried to get out of the window but I felt hands on me and someone had me by the waist and was lifting me off the floor and the walls and ceiling went spinning around and I thought I saw faces in the doorway and then I was in the air and crashing into the wall and I blacked out.

Chapter
NINETEEN

I was on the operating table for four hours while they put my shoulder back together. Later on, Alan told me that when I hit the wall, my shoulder split the long way. He showed me the X-ray; that thin white line went from just below my right ear all the way out almost to the end of the shoulder bone. Another quarter of an inch, Alan said, and my shoulder would have been in two pieces and they would have had to use steel pins and I would have been in a cast for six months.

He had really tried to kill me; there was no doubt in my mind. I can still see that face coming at me and feel the belt buckle cutting into me. The people living on the same floor had heard the nurse screaming out in the hall and they had called the doorman. It took three men—the doorman, the handyman, and one of the neighbors—to get Brace off me. Later on, when I went back to the apartment to get my things, the doorman asked me how I was. He told me he would never forget to his dying day how I had sailed through the air and how the plaster cracked when I hit the wall.

For six weeks I had my right arm strapped down to my side and my neck and shoulder in a cast. The cuts healed slowly because some of them were deep and needed stitches but only one or two left scars which included the one on my cheek, just my luck; but when I get my settlement, plastic surgery will take care of that.

Alan got word to my sister Angie and the family rallied around and came to the rescue. Marcie took care of Danny and my dog Jackie and Angie was at the hospital every day. She got me a lawyer to sue Brace for damages, and for a separation, too. This time there was no pressure from above or anybody calling anybody up in the middle of the night to tell him he was going to have his arms and legs broken. None of that crap, because Gordon was out of ATA, voted out by the board of directors, and the F.C.C. was investigating the whole ATA-network setup, and, of course, Brace was out with Gordon because the agency had replaced him on all the shows he was doing

216

and nobody in New York and Hollywood was even talking to him, let alone doing him favors.

I lay there in the hospital and read the stories that came out in the papers about the wild orgies that used to go on after hours in Gordon's offices, and I knew that Brace must have been in on them. Secretaries and stenographers and vice-presidents and television stars, they had all been in on them, and it was men with girls and men with men and girls with girls, the works, and all the girls working up there had keys to the men's rooms and the guys had keys to the ladies' rooms. I read about the heads rolling up at ATA and at the networks, and it sounded more like a couple of competing bowling alleys than an agency-network setup and, natch, one of the girls who was fired sold her memoirs to the *Daily News* and they ran it in installments and it covered a lot of ground about the men Gordon liked to have around him and how they used to date each other and all about the jealous fights that went on over interoffice phones and behind closed doors. And, of course, guess whose name was there in big, black letters like the captain of the team? Would you believe, Mr. Brace Fontaine? And then, of course, that brought up the story of Danny's christening party, poor kid, what a thing to have hung around his neck at that age, and the paper picked up the fact that I was suing for divorce and before the fuss died down one of the news magazines did a big spread on the big agency scandal. A newspaper photographer tried to get a picture of me all bandaged up in the hospital before Alan came in and had him kicked out, but the next day his paper called and bought an exclusive from me. I appreciated Alan's protecting me like that, but a girl has to eat, especially a girl with a kid to support, and somehow I had to put my life back together, what there was left of it.

Joye came to see me three times, the first time with Sam.

"How are you doing, Ace?" Sam said, and that was all he said all the time they were there. They were both shocked by what Brace had done to me and what had happened and I think it was a terrible blow to them when Brace just cut them completely and disappeared out of their lives. The second time Joye came alone with a bulky envelope under her arm. It turned out to be the page proofs of her book and she left them with me to read even though, she said, no one was supposed to see them but her, but she wanted my opinion. I went through them in a day, one revealing, surprising day. The book was all about show business, just as Joye had said it would be, and it went back and forth from New York to Hollywood. The main character was a guy just like Gordon, only he had a different name, and a lot of the things he did and what happened to him were incidents I had given her. Brace and I were both in it, under different names, of course, but you could recognize us and our marriage and there was a lot of in stuff about people and places and incidents that she had never known but that I had described to her. When I finished reading it, I just lay back in the bed and closed my eyes and laughed, because now I knew what all the long afternoon talks were really about.

"Come on, let's have some girl talk!"

Shit!

The third time she came it was to pick up the proofs, but I think it really was to see if I was mad at her or wanted to sue or something. I didn't do anything like that and I wasn't really mad; maybe surprised and maybe a little hurt, which I still am, but not mad. I told her I thought it was a helluva book, which it was, and that I hoped it would make her a lot of money and I thought it would make a great movie, which it did. And she looked relieved and grateful and kissed me with tears in her eyes and went home happy.

My lawyers got me a separation and had Danny put into my custody and made Brace pay the hospital bills. Then Dolores asked me if I would like to move in and live with her and Mom. Mom was fading away a little faster each day and Dolores had her hands full with her, but she wasn't complaining and there was plenty of room. I knew I couldn't go back to the apartment and there was no place else for me to go anyway, so I told her I would. I could have moved in with Alan. He offered to take me and Danny until I could find my own place. I told him that I didn't have any income, and with a baby to take care of, there wouldn't be any until I could leave him with somebody and go out to work and that would leave Alan stuck with us for months. Anyhow, my lawyer said no when he heard about it because Alan wasn't married and Brace could maybe bring a countersuit against me and that would be bad for the divorce and the settlement.

Then Alan asked me to marry him. He said that he would be satisfied if I got a Mexican divorce and the hell with any settlement, because if I married anybody before that came through I would lose most of it. He said that he

218

would pay for the divorce and buy a house out in the suburbs . . . start a practice and make a mint like all suburban doctors, and we could have a great life together. Isn't that the way with me? Every time I look around there's some other guy wanting to shell out for me. Anyhow, you can't starve that way, right? But, of course, Alan isn't like the others. He's no jerkoff. He's a really sincere sweet guy and I dug him a lot but not to go to bed with him, at least not then while I was walking around in that damn cast like Henry Armetta. Skip it, you wouldn't know him.

I almost took Alan up on it. I asked him for a few days to think it over and I did, very seriously, because a girl doesn't get a proposal like that every day. I mean, Alan was security in spades for the rest of my life. Maybe I wouldn't be living in the lap of luxury, but I would never have to worry about a thing again and Danny would have a good home and go to school and college, not like his mother who never even finished ninth grade, and our lives would be taken care of right there and then. All I had to do was say yes. And then Jerry called. Wouldn't you know it? Any time I was in a bind of some kind, who came along on his big white horse? Right, my shining cherry-picking knight in armor, Jerry Miller.

He called from Hollywood, natch—where else does he ever call from? He had read all about the scandal and me splitting up with Brace and my being in the hospital and he was very concerned about me as per usual. A funny thing happened to me while I was talking to him. When I first heard his voice, so help me, I felt the old excitement all over again. That's right, the torch was still burning and I think it is even to this day. But the longer he talked and the more I listened, the louder I could hear my friend, that little bell in the back of my head, going *ting! ting!* like a fire alarm.

This time I paid more attention to the bell than to Jerry, and when he said, "Listen, I'm going to be back in New York next month. You should be out of the hospital by then so how about having lunch with me and let's talk," I said, "What are we going to talk about?"

He hesitated for just a minute and then he said, very low into the phone, like a crooner singing to his middle-aged fans, "You and me, of course."

I said to myself, Oh, no, here we go again.

"Jerry," I said, "how long will you be in New York?"

"About a week," he said. "Why?"

219

"And what happens after the week?"

"I go back to Hollywood. Why?"

"Do Danny and I go to Hollywood with you?"

There was a long pause at his end and then he said, "Danny ... oh, you mean the kid! Well, now, look, Nina, you know I travel around a lot and taking a kid along would be murder, you know that!"

"Sure, I know that," I told him. "And you're right, it would be murder. Thanks for calling, Jerry."

"Wait, Nina! Hold it a minute!"

"Jerry, I have to hang up. The nurse wants the bedpan," which was the first thing I could think of. How would that grab you, you Romeos out there in televisionland, if you were talking to some chick on the phone trying to set her up for a bang and you found out that she'd been taking a shit while you were talking to her.

"Look, call me when you get to town," I told him, "and we'll talk over the phone again, right? And thanks for calling, Jerry."

It was starting right then, the way I treat jerkoffs who try to get into me. I don't have much patience with them and that goes for Jerry, too, much as I torch for him. He never tried that on me again. Of course he doesn't call me very often anymore, not that he ever really did, and when he does he may beat around the bush a little but he never tries to screw me.

When it came to putting up the ante in Alan's game, I passed. Even though I hadn't fallen for Jerry's line, talking to him had started me thinking and I knew that Alan Stone was not for me. Security or not, I just couldn't see myself tied down in a home somewhere out in suburbia, keeping house and raising kids and the same thing day after day in the same way with him jumping up at three in the morning to run out to a patient, and the three weeks every year in the summer bungalow! I mean, for some girls I'm sure that's just what they want, but not this girl. There just has to be more to it than that, or else why did I go through all that shit? Is that the whole story for a woman? Maybe for some, but not for me, because if there's one thing I realized that I had learned it was how to stay alive and going in a world of men. I think I learned that the first time that I had to face up to a club owner when I was twelve and tell him that we wouldn't sing another show until he had our john cleaned and smelling nice. I will admit that I was an awful jerk when it came to men and sex and love, that's for sure, and it

220

took me a long time to find my way around in that ballgame, but I finally did and now I don't buy that love shit anymore, and when I go to bed with a man it's because I want to get laid and he's the guy I want to lay me at that particular moment, understand?

Besides that, I knew that I had a beautiful face and a body that makes men drool and that I can get them to give to me without me giving to them, and that's one way of staying alive and going. And I knew that I had a damn good voice, an exciting voice, and I knew how to hold an audience and make them stand up and cheer, and that's another way of staying alive and going. And I knew that I had a brain and it was working all the time thinking and putting thoughts together and creating, and that's still another way of staying alive and going. And best of all and most of all I had Danny and that was the biggest reason of all for staying alive and going, but what a cop-out it would be if I married Alan and settled for security without being able to be myself all the way.

Alan was very disappointed when I told him, because I really think he loved me even if there were big differences between us in the way we thought and the things we liked to do. I really think I did the guy a favor, because can you imagine a nice, quiet, conservative doctor sitting around in clubs and restaurants till all hours of the morning? And I love that kind of life, I really do, except, of course, I don't have much of it anyway, do I? Except when some jerkoff like Herbie asks me out to build his image, right?

To make this long story a little shorter, I moved in with Dolores. Angie picked me up when I left the hospital. Alan put me into her car and leaned in through the window to kiss me good-bye and said to come to him whenever I needed help. I had called beforehand and made sure that Brace wasn't around, because the first stop we made was back at the apartment. My separation said that I was entitled to my clothes but not the jewelry which had to be fought over in court. I filled three big valises with all the evening gowns and shoes and the pants suits that were just coming in then and that I had bought just before the split. And when the valises were in the car, I went back up and took out my furs in my arms, not forgetting the muffs. Before I closed the door behind me for the last time, I looked around the place, not burning down the old nostalgia but glad I was leaving. I had seen the bedroom wall where the plaster wasn't repaired yet, and that was enough in itself to send me away without tears.

Our next stop was at Marcie's where we picked up the dog and Danny, poor baby. I'm glad he didn't know what was going on at that time. The only thing he knew was that he had to go on formula because his momma couldn't hold him to nurse with her shoulder in a cast. Then we drove up to Haverstraw, and Danny and I moved in with Mom and Dolores.

Mom lasted only three weeks. Watching her die a little each day like that wasn't the best experience in the world for me after what I had been through, but she had a chance to see her grandson for the last few days of her life. I couldn't deny her that, and I had a chance to do something for her and get my mind off myself for a while. At the end, on the last day, when she lay there fighting for life and not making it, I couldn't stand to watch anymore. I ran out of the house and into the garage that used to be a barn and I sat there on an old wooden crate where I couldn't hear the noise of her breath forcing its way in and out of her open mouth slower and slower and slower, and I tried to remember her sitting by the kitchen window eating bread sprinkled with sugar or moving around the kitchen making *cecira e pasta,* or the way she looked sitting in the kitchen chair waiting when we came home with Pop late at night from some club date. When I heard my sisters crying I walked back inside and up to her room and I kissed her for the last time.

After she was buried and we had all chipped in as much as we could for her funeral and a stone, I applied for relief. I could see that the divorce was going to drag on for years because Brace was fighting me every inch of the way. He had everything tied up, so what else could I do? Oh, I know, I could have hocked my furs, but the few thousand dollars I would have gotten would have been spent in a year, and then what would I have had? At least I had the muffs to put my hands into and bring back my mother and I had the coats to look at and wear once in a while in the privacy of my bedroom and dream of making it again in show business and getting out of Haverstraw and back into my own pad, just me and Danny.

Because that's what I really want. That's what I'm working for. As long as there are agencies and networks and managers around for me to talk to and send material to, that's what I'm aiming for! Listen, it's not so bad even being on welfare. I'm still sweating out the divorce settlement, which should give me a lot of shekels when it comes through, and I know I'll have to pay back all the money I've been collecting from welfare, but I'll still have a big pile left. In the meantime I have Danny to take care of, which I love doing, and my dog Jackie to love me the way only a dog loves you without asking anything in return for it, and I've got these jerkoffs hanging around to keep my morale up. Nothing will ever come out of those idiots. The sooner they realize I'm not laying for any of them the better. Except maybe Herbie. Something might happen with Herbie. But I don't know, I've told you all about him, and when I listen to you give him back to me, he doesn't add up to a helluva lot, does he? I guess Danny is all I really want. I've had enough of the other kind of life, all that shit that goes on. Who needs that? Oh, maybe someday some guy will come along who's not a jerkoff, who doesn't see me as just a beautiful body he'd like to rub up against and push into, someone like Alan, maybe, who's solid and strong enough to give himself and not just take. And if he doesn't come—well, that's all right, too. Yes, I know, Danny will grow up and go off on his own one of these days, and then where will I be? Alone with no one around to remember what a doll I was once and tell me so and still love me, for all the shadows and wrinkles hanging around my eyes and mouth. What the hell! Who needs men? I've had it with men. Like the old song said, I get along without them very well. I've got myself, which is the best company in the world, and I've got you. You're really all I need besides Danny. Only to tell you the truth, one of these days I won't even need you. I'll have all the answers and you'll just sit there dumb and never say anything to me again, because there won't be anything left to say. When that day comes, and it will, that will be the end of a beautiful friendship, because that's when I pull out the plug.